THE HARP AND THE FERRYMAN

Helen Cox and Peter Roberts

To Jill in friendship.
love
Helen Cox
x x

MICHELLE ANDERSON PUBLISHING
MELBOURNE

First published in Australia 2013 by
Michelle Anderson Publishing Pty Ltd
P O Box 6032 Chapel Street North
South Yarra 3141 Melbourne, Australia
Email: mapubl@bigpond.net.au
Website: www.michelleandersonpublishing.com
Tel: 62 3 9826 9028

Cover design: Chameleon Print Design
Cover photograph: nitchphotography
Typeset by: Midland Typesetters, Australia
Printed by: Toppan Security Printing Pte. Ltd.

National Library of Australia cataloguing-in-publication entry
Author: Cox, Helen.
Title: The harp and the ferryman/Helen Cox, Peter Roberts.
ISBN: 9780855724283 (pbk.)
Subjects: Music thanatology.
            Music Therapy
            Palliative Treatment
            Harp music—Therapeutic use
Other Authors/Contributors:
            Roberts, Peter.

Dewey Number: 615.85154

The lines 'I am calling to you . . .' quoted by permission of The Golden Sufi Centre, copyright © 1998, from *Catching the Thread: Sufism, Dreamwork, and Jungian Psychology* by Llewellyn Vaughan-Lee. www.goldensufi.org Print permission 9 March 2011; ebook permission 17 February 2012.

The Reed Flute Song and quotes from *The Essential Rumi* by Coleman Barks used with permission from Coleman Barks, 2 March 2011.

The lines 'Can you be with me in the cold morning of dying?' quoted with permission from Phyllida Anam-Aire through rights manager/editor Sabine Weeks, Findhorn Press, 2 May 2012.

The authors have made every attempt to portray the events and stories within the book as faithfully as possible.

Praise for The Harp and the Ferryman

My life and work focuses on the scientific evidence base for healthcare; this book presents evidence on the effects of the work of Peter Roberts on the lives (and deaths) of others that is just as powerful as any multi-site randomised clinical trial. This beautifully written; stunningly engaging; and powerfully challenging book provides a cogent account of the work of a harpist with dying people and with premature infants. It presents the evidence to support the assertion that music is therapeutic and that it heals in the broadest sense of the word. This well crafted story of a music-thanatologist and the examination and evaluation of his work with the dying and with babies in a neonatal unit represents the best – and most moving – read I have ever had.

Professor Alan Pearson AM
Faculty of Health Sciences
The University of Adelaide, South Australia.

The Harp and the Ferryman tells a story of Peter's personal journey: having the courage to leave everything you know to pursue a dream and the 'leadings of the spirit'. Peter's work in accompanying dying and other sick people is clearly a thing of beauty and benefit. His personal and spiritual journey is one of courage and emotion. It a powerful human story for a general audience, especially for readers who have an interest in spirituality and pastoral care.

Professor Michael Ashby
Director of Palliative Care.
Southern Area Health Service and Royal Hobart Hospital.
Professor of Palliative Care, University of Tasmania, Australia.

The *Harp and the Ferryman* describes Peter Robert's extraordinary transformation from a dealer in fine furniture to a music-thanatologist. It is a journey of self-discovery. A journey in which his outer world slowly falls apart and then aligns itself with a deep-seated longing to play the harp and sing for those whose pain is beyond the reach of conventional medicine. This is a hauntingly beautiful insight into one man's dream to step into the unknown and follow the music of his heart. The book will change you just as Peter's music transforms the lives of others.

Dr Michael Barbato
Palliative care physician and consultant, Australia.
Author Reflections of a Setting Sun and Caring for the Living and Dying.

The Harp and the Ferryman

One of the most humane and effective therapies that has arisen in recent years to help the dying in their transition is music-thanatology. *The Harp and the Ferryman* is an insider's view of this marvelous intervention can provide comfort and hope in life's final moments.

Larry Dossey, MD
Executive Director Explore: The Journal of Science and Healing.
Author: Space, Time & Medicine; Beyond Illness; Recovering the Soul;
Meaning and Medicine; Reinventing Medicine. *USA*

We all expect help when a new baby is born. It seems a fundamental right. But who in our society provides that same level of highly skilled and intimate care for the dying?

There is an urgent need to address the quality of death in a society preoccupied with the quality of life. This much-needed book makes an invaluable contribution as Peter and Helen point out poetically musical new possibilities.

Read this book and change the way you view dying; maybe even change the way you approach death itself.

Ian Gawler OAM
Gawler Foundation, Australia.
Author of The Mind that Changes Everything; Peace of Mind;
The Dragon's Blessing; *and* You Can Conquer Cancer

I was not familiar with music-thanatology but the descriptions in this book of Peter's presence and his music are very convincing and deeply touching to read. This is a book that should be read and discussed by health personnel, especially those in the field of palliative care who are open to innovative therapeutic approaches.

Professor Kristin Heggen,
Faculty of Medicine
University of Oslo, Norway

The Harp and the Ferryman offers readers a unique combination of rigorous, innovative research and transformative stories about the healing power of music. It is a remarkable account of Peter Roberts' life-changing call, and the patients who benefit daily from his musicality and presence. *The Harp and the Ferryman* will leave you moved by the work of this extraordinary man, and longing to hear his music for yourself.

Jennifer L. Hollis, MDiv, CM-Th
Former President, Music-Thanatology Association
International (2006–2012). USA
Author, Music at the End of Life: Easing the Pain and Preparing the Passage

The Harp and the Ferryman

Helen Cox invites the reader to become an 'existential insider'; travelling with dying patients on their final journey, accompanied by Peter Roberts' plaintive harp music. Music-thanatology comes alive as we join the ferryman gently steering newborn babies, hospice patients and nursing-home residents across the river. This book takes us to the heart of palliative care; where 'annointing people with sound' transforms body, mind and spirit in the presence of death.

Associate Professor Rosalie Hudson
School of Nursing & Social Work
The University of Melbourne, Australia.

The concept of harmony takes on a whole new richness of meaning when you read of the wonderful connectedness that Peter Roberts shares through his harp with patients and their loved ones. His story of being drawn to the field of music-thanatology mirrors the manner in which those in need of soothing and uplifting are drawn to his music. The tears you shed reading this book are due to the sharing of emotion and calm pleasures, not sadness. I am incredibly grateful that Helen and Peter have allowed us this insight into such a such a world of love and understanding.

Dr Yvonne Luxford
Chief Executive Officer
Palliative Care Australia Incorporated

This is a remarkable story. A man with a harp and a soft voice brings solace to dying people. The same person plays soothing music to premature babies, to anxious parents and to hospital staff under stress. It is a simple and good story, and everyone who reads it will be astounded, astonished, and amazed! Peter Roberts is a music-thanatologist. Like the ferryman on the mythic River Styx, his music carries people across the gulf from life to death. It would also be appropriate to call him a life-ologist because it is the most critical moments of life that his music so beautifully transforms.

In the book, Helen Cox, a professor of nursing, brings a critical and sympathetic research eye to observe this man at his work, and to measure the effects music has on babies and adults, many of whom are oblivious to other human communication. As a story, it must fall into a rare class; as a research project, 'the first of its kind in the world'. Above all else, it gives a glimpse of the best humanity, as one man sits quietly with people 'at their lowest point and then slowly and gradually, with his presence and his music,' brings them up again. Wrote Helen Cox: 'It was awesome in the truest sense.' The book is a salutary reminder to everyone of how a good presence and a quiet holding environment can be a vital experience for everyone. The harp and the music are beautiful parts of the story, but most of us will only have the good presence. That is a good place for all of us to start. How important it is!

Dr Francis Macnab AM, OM, PhD, DSc, DD
Executive Minister St Michaels Uniting Church, Melbourne
Founding Director Cairnmiller Institute, Australia.

Having known of the work of Peter Roberts for many years, it was a great pleasure to read this book, which so beautifully documents his personal journey of discovery, in tandem with demonstrating the evidence of his work.

Woven between the autobiographical details of Peter's life is the story of Helen Cox, who, it seems, was destined to meet Peter and be the co-writer of this book. She worked with little funding to produce evidence of the impact of music on vulnerable people, the first time this research has been undertaken.

The book is a testimony to a man who followed his heart and consequently has touched so many lives, mostly at a time of vulnerability and sadness. In applying the image of the ferryman to describe people's journeys to death, the image is just as applicable to the journey of Roberts himself. The story holds much pain and suffering as Roberts, together with his family, set out on a journey with an unknown end. Out of the frustration and pain has emerged a man with unique skills and an intuitive ability to meet others in their pain. Maybe it will inspire readers who have that deep niggling desire to do/be something else, to have the courage to begin their own journey of discovery.

Prof Margaret O'Connor AM. DN, MN, B.Theol, FRCNA, MAICD
Vivian Bullwinkel Chair in Palliative Care Nursing
Monash University, Melbourne, Australia.

The Harp and the Ferryman is the remarkable story of the foundation of music-thanatology in Australia as told by Helen Cox and Peter Roberts. Using personal reflections and patient stories, they share the extraordinary impact of Peter's sacred ministry for the sick, dying, and bereaved. This amazing book opens your heart to the mystery of death and the healing power of love through music.

Ruth Stanley, OSB, PharmD, MA, FASHP
CentraCare Heart and Vascular Center
Minnesota, USA.

The Harp and the Ferryman

Often synchronicities, the meaningful coincidences we experience, seem merely a lark or a twinkle from the cosmos. In *The Harp and the Ferryman*, the reader becomes fascinated with how these serendipitous events lead Peter Roberts to a most unlikely but rewarding path in life. Following one's inner voice is not always easy, especially when it involves uprooting a family. I picture Robert Frost hovering over Peter Roberts whispering, 'Two roads diverged in a wood, and I took the one less traveled by and that has made all the difference.'

The tale unfolds in modern day settings of hospitals, universities and continents and by the shores of the Corio Bay. The inspiriting sound of the harp through the mist while at the brink of the water can melt struggles like a beacon of light bringing the ferryman to shore. Learning how to trust and follow our dreams can build us into those same beacons of light for those in need around us. Touching lives each day, Peter's life still holds many synchronicities to come, for the heavens are not only winking, they are blinking with each string of compassion that he bestows upon patients with his harp. Indeed he is a 'harp specialist' – or rather, is that 'heart specialist'?

Christina Tourin
Director, International Harp Therapy Program
Music Therapist, USA.

This work is a journey of healing by two remarkable people who tell their stories of converging connections that take them and the reader into sacred spaces of music, sound and silence. Their own stories combined with their experiences with patients take these authors into realms of wonder. They each share the life world of amazing connections, which brought them and their work together. In turn this story of *The Harp and the Ferryman* becomes both a literal and living metaphor for the deeply personal/professional transformative experiences for dying patients and their families.

This inner life story of the two authors takes us into their spirit-filled life experiences and personal risks to follow their hearts, heads, talents and callings, where we get to relive their journey from the inside out. Thus we experience their beauty and gift of healing through their sacred presence and sound. Their result: an offering of formal practices of music, voice, sound and authentic presence for persons who are nearing death, yet hanging on, while perhaps longing for graceful passages from our Earth plane to conscious dying, letting go for serene passage to the other side of the Veil.

The Harp and the Ferryman

Ferryman and harp metaphors become a living story of living, dying and holding sacred space for mystery and miracles. Aside from the inner journey of this book, it also stands out for the style of writing and evocative originality, engaging the reader in the timeless life journey, helping readers to enter into the sacred circle of life and cross the threshold of the mystery of dying.

Jean Watson, PhD, RN, AHN-BC, FAAN
Distinguished Professor and Dean Emerita
University of Colorado, Denver
Founder, Watson Caring Science Institute, USA.

This enchanting book beautifully combines rich personal stories from the authors, accounts of the impact of music at death and dying with a scholarly research base. It is finely written and full of well-grounded wisdom and practice drawn from rich experience – a tale well told, readable for its own sake yet eminently informative, full of inspiration for healing and spiritual awakening. The authors skillfully, imaginatively and compassionately take us to that hard edge of life where suffering can seem hopeless and intractable, yet yields to courageous and heartfelt options, full of the potential for finding peace, wholeness, meaning and transformation. Inspiring and heartwarming.

Rev Prof Steve Wright
Chairman & Co Founder Sacred Space Foundation
Associate Professor Faculty of Health and Social Care
University of Cumbria, UK.

Foreword

This is a book of reverence. A book which pays homage to all of those who have been present to the healing power of music – be they professional or patient. The breadth of musical genre presented here reaches out beyond the boundaries of what science offers to the deeper places often hidden in life and sometimes painfully exposed as we face into our dying. The description of vigil as a sense of waiting in anticipation resonates with the reflections of the founder of the modern hospice movement, Cicely Saunders, in her little book *Watch with Me*, where she shows how our presence can be a powerful healing tool, possibly the most powerful tool of all. The careful presentation of the experiences of Helen as a nurse and researcher and Peter as a music-thanatologist build a compelling case for the value of music as a way to be present at that most challenging and painful of times for all of us. This book will make you want to know more. *The Harp and The Ferryman* evokes the tone and timbre of the life journey of Peter through his spiritual explorations which continue to give vitality to his role as a music-thanatologist. Moreover, the potential reach of music across the spectrum of healthcare, from neonatology to gerontology, gives a lasting image of new ways in which we as healthcare professionals can be truly present to those we care for in a meaningful and responsive way.

This book would be of benefit to a wide readership. Student nurses would learn greatly from Helen's reflections on nursing. Palliative care specialists and colleagues working in the complementary and supportive services will understand a little more about their sense of purpose in what they do every day. And for the public, this book will bring pleasure. That even at times which we fear most, such as dying, we need not be afraid of the 'aloneness' which the authors describe in such a meaningful way. The cases which are presented show us the importance of respecting sacred moments. The decisions that Peter Roberts made about where his life was going, have profoundly affected the lives of others. Wouldn't that be a wonderful legacy for all of us to leave behind when our time comes to die?

Dr Phil Larkin
Professor of Clinical Nursing (Palliative Care)
University College Dublin and Our Lady's Hospice and
Care Services,
Dublin, Ireland.

Contents

Prelude

Joan lies back in the bed. A small tear tracks from the corner of her eye and disappears into the pillow. She has been staring at the window, thinking about the difference between looking at it and looking through it: to look at the window is to look at what is directly in front of her; to look through the window is to look at what is beyond, and she can't focus enough to do the latter. The difference begins to obsess her because she is desperate to see the gum trees in flower, but the window only shows the rub marks of ineffective cleaning. She is dying. She has no time left to look at rub marks when the trees are in flower, but the switch takes so much energy.

Beyond holds more than the gum trees, though, and she knows that if she seeks the flowers she will see the rest. She wants to look but she is frightened. She remembers how she used to look at scary movies through her fingers, or from the safety of her mother's arms when she was small. Now there is no mother and her fingers have no magic.

The chaplain enters. He is a lean, serious man with black hair that falls over one eye. He sits beside the bed and notices the tear track on Joan's cheek.

'Hello,' he says quietly, slipping his hand under hers.

She squeezes it slightly, as much as she can manage, and smiles in recognition. She whispers, 'I don't know what to do.'

He knows what she means. She has said this before, that death is just out there, just outside the window where the trees are and she has no idea how to greet it or how to stop being here and start being there.

Joan feels like she is standing at the edge of an ocean. Between jagged breaths she says to the chaplain, 'I know I have to cross it if I'm to get there, but I can't work out how to. I don't know how to . . . I can't just step off. I need someone to show me, or take me.'

She asks if she has to cross, because she is not sure she really wants to go where crossing would take her, or if she should turn away. And if she turns away, will it make any difference? Will it stop this thing that is just outside the window? Deep down she knows there really isn't any choice for her now, but she simply does not know what to do.

'Don't do anything,' the chaplain says. 'Just rest, just breathe, in and out, slowly, in and out.' He sits with her for a while, breathing with her, praying for her. 'Just respond to the moment. Try to trust that it will be all right.' Eventually he leaves.

A couple of hours later there is a muted knock on Joan's door. A man pushes a harp through the doorway, introduces himself as the hospital musician. He asks if she would like him to play for her for a little while. She is exhausted, but also curious. Besides, she loves music. She nods.

The man pulls up a chair beside her bed and he tells her his name is Peter. 'I'll just play quietly for you,' he says. 'If you want to go to sleep, that's fine. If you want to just relax and listen, that's fine too.'

He plays a tune Joan does not recognise. She is resting her head on the pillow, watching his hands on the strings. She has always loved the harp, though there is no harp music in her collection. She looks at the instrument and feels drawn to run her hands over its silkiness, its sweeping curves.

Joan asks what the tune is.

Peter replies that it is one of his own compositions called 'The Ferryman'. He tells her the words:

Carry me ferryman . . . over the water,
Carry me ferryman . . . over the sea,
Carry me homeward . . . for my love is calling me,
Carry me ferryman . . . over the sea.

The musician says that he doesn't usually sing the words when he plays in the hospital and then he puts the words and melody together for her, singing softly as he plucks the notes on his harp.

She is silent. Eyes closed, she is listening.

'I had an image in my mind when I wrote it,' he tells her. 'There's a young woman whose yearning has brought her to a misty rendezvous at the water's edge. The yearning she feels is to reunite with her beloved. She is separated from the source of this inner calling by the seemingly impassable stretch of water. But there at the shore a roughly dressed boatman is waiting for her with a small boat. He has come to meet her.'

Joan is listening. A nurse comes in to do a treatment, but Joan puts her hand up. 'Not now.'

Peter continues. 'The rough ferryman who has come to take her over the water is really her disguised lover, who understood the calling and in fact was its source. He was patiently waiting there for her to respond. And now he rows to her, the oars dipping, the boat gliding. She doesn't know it yet, but her yearning has been fulfilled. He has come to carry her home.'

Once more, Peter plays and sings his ferryman song.

Joan is listening deeply, intensely. She can see the oars gliding through the water, each stroke taking the lovers out further, and then, as Peter plays a section in a minor key, he tells her that this is where they disappear into the mist.

Joan's eyes spring open and she turns her head to him. 'This is what I'm scared of,' she says with a catch in her throat.

He understands. He works with people who are dying. He understands the fear. He touches her arm. 'Ah, but it resolves,' he replies, and he plays further into the tune to show her how, until Joan grows peaceful. He plays a little longer and then, quietly, he leaves.

Joan is not asleep. She is thinking, but her breathing is slower and more even and there is softness in her eyes. The story has evoked a memory of her own: there was a man once, long gone now, but he had been so important, the most important person in her life. She turns her head to the window, imagining him, a wispy figure on the other side of the glass. There is no struggle now to look through the glass. It is easy. Some barrier has been lifted. She is not sad at the memory, but she pulls his shadowy face into focus with her need and his eyes look at her with love. His eyes stay clear in her mind as she drifts off to sleep. She dreams of a small boat. The music fades into the lapping water.

The next day the chaplain returns and sits quietly by her bed again. Joan is sleeping. He looks at her gaunt face and the dark hollows under her eyes. She is still a youngish woman, not yet sixty, and he knows the end is close. He is not afraid of death and he does not wish it away for her. He will offer what he can.

She stirs and opens her eyes to find him there. She smiles a welcome to this man whose gentleness and simplicity have been so comforting. She tells him about the musician who came yesterday, and the story of the song. She has spoken to the chaplain before about the man who left so long ago and he knows her grief. He sees what the song has evoked but he also sees that she has a little spark in her eye, some energy. He finds her different; he realises that her fear has gone.

She takes his hands, and he notes a little strength in her fingers.

'He came for me,' she tells him. 'He was here and he carried me. I am on the other side now. I am there, and I am ready.'

He smiles.

Section 1

ℬ'

The Healing Power of Music

Helen

1

ℛ'

Getting Involved

Somewhere around the age of fifty-two and never having played a musical instrument in my life, I fell in love with the harp. I bought a 36-string levered Lyon and Healy troubadour. Tall, made of pale blond, smoothly curving beech, it stands elegantly in the little room I had dedicated to books and silence. Now, touched by music, what was a quiet room – peaceful but kind of reserved – feels a little lighter.

Having found a harp, I embarked on a journey to find a teacher. I met Jacinta Dennett in 1998 when she performed for the Barwon Heads Fine Music Society on a balmy Saturday evening in March. On the following day I discovered her busking in the midst of the noise and mess of a street market. How amazing to see this accomplished orchestral harpist busking. It gave me the chance to sit entranced and, in a lull, to ask her to be my teacher. Buying the harp and finding a teacher were the first of a series of coincidences that led to the writing of this book.

A few years into my harp love affair, I hunted through the racks of CDs in the Theosophical Society Bookshop in

Melbourne and found a CD called *Love and the Ferryman*, by a harpist named Peter Roberts. I studied the picture on the cover: just a simple wooden jetty worn by the elements, and just off the jetty, a small wooden rowboat bobbing in the water. The pale sunlight reflects in the water and I notice a faint impression of a harp and hands brushing the strings. There is a sense of serenity in the picture.

I listened to a few tracks through the large black earphones hanging on the wall and decided to buy it; the music was simple and sweet and Peter's voice light. The title of the CD made me think of Charon, the ferryman of Hades in Greek mythology, carrying the souls of the newly dead over the River Styx, the river that separates the worlds of the living and the dead. Stumbling across this music was the next coincidence that, as well as leading to this book, led to a change of direction for me.

Then, only days later while scanning *The Age* newspaper, a photograph of a man playing a harp caught my attention. It was Peter Roberts playing a harp at the bedside of a woman in hospital. Reading the article I learned that Peter had a contract to play the harp at the St John of God Hospital Geelong, where he is called a 'therapeutic musician'. Now I could connect the man to the music and discovered that he was involved in healthcare and played in particular for people who were dying. I wondered whether he thought of himself somehow in connection to Charon. Was that why he titled the CD *The Ferryman*?

Reading the article caused me to reflect on some of my nursing encounters with dying people; some with a sense of reverence, others chaotic and filled with struggle. I have cared for countless dying people over the years and could imagine how music might change the experience of dying, both for the person dying and those who keep vigil alongside. I thought that just having this presence in the room could change everything about the environment for the person who was dying, and for me too. I could imagine the sound of the harp helping me to connect with the person I was caring for in a deeper, even more compassionate way.

The next thing that happened in this unfolding story occurred one Tuesday afternoon in the autumn of 2004. The telephone rang while I was sitting in my office at the Epworth Hospital behind a glass wall that separated me from my research assistant and secretary. I had been struggling with a research grant application that I was writing. The form was complex, repetitive and irritating. I stopped typing and gazed out of the window, turning my attention away from the wretched form for a moment. Beyond the window, beyond the corridor that connected the foyer to the lifts that rose to the executive offices, was a courtyard with a cluster of silver birch trees and under their canopy, hundreds of glorious hellebores with their shy mauve and green flowers hiding amongst the leaves. I often walked among them and have planted a patch in a dappled area of my garden at home. That courtyard was the only place for smokers because of the hospital's no-smoking policy, so there were cigarette butts everywhere, which certainly detracted from the beauty. From my vantage point, though, the butts were invisible. It was a little oasis in my irritation.

I half listened as my secretary answered, put the caller on hold and buzzed me. 'It's Dr Sarah Leach,' she said.

I was surprised. Sarah was a research fellow working between Deakin University's School of Nursing and Midwifery and the St John of God Hospital Geelong. I took the call, curious to know why she would be calling me at Epworth in Melbourne, and that was the next coincidence. All of these would converge.

'Hi Sarah, what can I do for you?'

She told me about a small grant that had become available in the Geelong region through Kings Australia, leaders in the funeral industry. 'They're looking for innovative projects,' she said. 'They have several areas of interest but the one that jumped out at me was advancement of care to clients. I want to target that one.'

I was a bit perplexed. My image of things that are of interest to nurses includes dying but does not generally include funerals. I asked her what she had in mind.

She started to tell me about Peter Roberts. 'Peter is a music-thanatologist,' she said.

I told her that I had heard about Peter but had never heard that term 'music-thanatologist'. What did it mean?

She replied that thanatology is the science of the study of death and the practices associated with it, and a music-thanatologist is someone who plays live harp at the bedside of people who are dying.

'I thought that we could put an application in to Kings to explore the effect of his work with people who are dying,' she said. 'Peter and I have been talking about it for a while. I told Peter about you and he thought it would be a good idea to ask if you would work with us, help us to write the application.'

I could hardly believe my ears. At that time I held a joint appointment as professor of nursing between Deakin University and the Epworth Hospital. My expertise was in qualitative research and it was that expertise Sarah wanted. I had never heard of music-thanatology, but I loved the harp and I was a passionate harp student. I knew of Peter because of the CD and the article in the newspaper, and I believed in the power of music. Intrigued, I said that I would be pleased to help.

We worked out a plan of attack and sent documents backwards and forwards fine tuning our application. We relied on

Telstra conference calls, and emails between Sarah and Peter in Geelong and me in Melbourne.

The project we developed was to implement and evaluate a music-thanatology program specifically in palliative care. We wanted to discover if, and in what ways, the people who experienced Peter's presence and his music found it useful. We intended to speak to patients, relatives and staff and would extend the study beyond the hospital if patients went home or were transferred somewhere else. The study would be done on days that Peter was not employed, paid for by the grant.

Our application titled 'An Australian project to implement and evaluate a live harp therapeutic music program in a palliative care setting' was successful. The people at Kings Australia who shortlisted and eventually decided on the grant winner knew Peter Roberts, respected his work and were pleased to support the beginning of an evidence base for it. We were delighted. Sarah steered the project through the ethics committee processes and got down to the business of employing a research assistant and starting the project. I kept in touch as adviser.

The project was not without perplexing issues. For example, there were serious recruitment problems, not unexpected since participants in the study were dying: focused inward with no patience for research, no energy left for anything other than the work that dying required of them. We had devoted a number of meetings to solving that dilemma and eventually we had hit on the idea of recruiting through pastoral services and not using the word 'research' but rather an evaluation of Peter's work with harp music in healthcare. People respond warmly to Peter and his music so recruitment was not an issue after that. Naturally, being in our study was not a condition of having Peter play for someone; it just meant that the researcher would not be present.

Because of the time spent solving problems, the funds attached to the researcher position were running out. It was evident that Sarah could no longer financially support the researcher Helen Fennessy, whom she had employed to collect the data for the project. She could not gather the data herself, since her work straddled two institutions and her time at the hospital was already full. I had the solution. I was about to retire and move back to Geelong to live. I offered to take on the role of researcher in a voluntary capacity and the offer was accepted.

With eight years elapsing between buying the harp and starting work on the research project, the convergence had finally occurred. I had discovered the harp, learned to play it under the tutelage of Jacinta Dennett, and my love of the harp led me to Peter Roberts, to music-thanatology and the research. Now that I was to be more closely involved, it was time for me to finally meet Peter.

2

✿

The Gallery Concert

Until I moved back to Geelong in 2005, I knew Peter from the CD, from press reports that appeared from time to time, and from his disembodied voice on the telephone in conference calls planning the Kings project. He knew my return to Geelong was imminent and that once I had unpacked I would commence in the researcher position on the project. Sarah told me he had some concerns about that. Knowing that I am a professor, he felt anxious that I might be scientifically inclined and not have the sensitivity required for understanding what he does. I knew the only way I could alleviate his concern would be through my actions as researcher. We planned to meet as soon as I could manage it.

Then my friends Anne and Brian Riggs alerted me to a concert featuring Peter Roberts to be held at the Geelong Art Gallery. The Saturday of the concert would be my first weekend back in Geelong so I decided to go. I did not tell Peter that I would be there; I decided just to experience his music and to introduce myself later.

The concert day arrived and I left my unpacked boxes, my husband and the chaos of my new home to drive to the gallery. Being a little early, I waited for Anne and Brian and when they arrived we wandered over to where a crowd was gathering. It was only a small crowd, perhaps thirty people seated in rows of chairs set out in a semicircle in the foyer to the left of the entrance. In front of the chairs stood a microphone, a chair and a harp. The carpeted foyer was hushed. Only one person attended the reception desk; being early on a Saturday morning the art lovers had not yet started to arrive. We sat toward the back at the edge of the semicircle.

Peter entered the room. A tall slender man, he was clean-shaven, with light brown hair and wearing an open-neck blue shirt and casual grey slacks. He sat, looked around the group and smiled a welcome to some he knew. He started to speak.

'Hello all, and thank you for coming. I'm not really sure what you expect from this morning. I'm not even sure what *I* expect.' He laughed. 'Let me tell you a little about what I do'. And then he proceeded to talk about music-thanatology. 'My work is mainly with people who are dying. I try to offer comfort and some peace. Often when people are close to death they struggle with trying to hang on. I try to help them to let go.'

I thought again of Charon.

He told us that he works at the St John of God Hospital. He emphasised that what he does is not about playing 'nice' music for comfort; he chooses what he plays carefully and it is generally not music that people are familiar with. There is serious intent behind what he does. He told us a story about one woman he had played for the previous week.

'The pieces of music I offered her were ancient sacred chants. I offered them as tenderly as I could. I was trying to offer gentle reverence and comfort for her using the music to lift her beyond this world into a beautiful place. I'm just picturing her as I'm speaking.' He paused for a moment and smiled as if at the memory. 'Her breathing was shallow and slow. She was very peaceful, raised to a place of peace and calm. Her breathing told me that she was there, and it was my intention to keep her in that place as long as I could. Hopefully she could leave from there.'

I had never heard anyone speak like that before, nor have such a total acceptance of death. Everyone was quiet.

He said that he would play for us, just a little so we could get a sense of his music. 'But I want this to be an interesting and maybe unusual experience for you. After I play a little, we'll move into the gallery. I would like you to wander around looking at the artwork, not paying any particular attention to me. In each room I'll position myself somewhere and will do something – sing or play an instrument. I'm not sure what. I'll decide when I'm there. I thought we could go on a little musical adventure together. Are you up for that?'

A murmur of assent went through the little group.

The soft clear sounds of the harp filled the air. Although I was a harpist myself with a large collection of harp music – classical, Celtic, folk and contemporary –I had never heard this music. I learned later that it was a piece he had composed. Now, after all these years, I know it well, and play it sometimes too.

His fingers moved lightly over the strings and I noticed his harp was left-handed. How strange, I thought. From the way he moved the chair and the harp into position I could see that he was actually right-handed. As he tipped the harp back, it rested on his left shoulder and he played melody with his left hand. My harp rests on my right shoulder and I play melody with my right hand. The levers on his harp were on the opposite side to mine. I watched and felt disoriented. I knew I could not make my way around this harp.

Then he shifted into familiar tunes, the mood still peaceful and serene. I closed my eyes and drifted into the music, the sounds of the harp as always so beautiful to me. He played for fifteen minutes or so. After a while, he placed the harp upright on the floor and motioned us to move into the gallery. He had asked us not to applaud anything he did, not wanting us to disturb the atmosphere. We filed into the first room with just a little bit of chatter as people commented on the harp music, marvelling at this thing called music-thanatology and wondering what lay ahead.

The pictures on the walls of this room were mainly landscapes: bushland, streams and mountains. Some were large with ornate gilt frames, others smaller and plainer. The room itself was large and airy; the impression was one of grandeur, a familiar feeling in galleries such as this. We moved about the room, studying the paintings.

Peter stood apart from us in a corner. He stood straight, closed his eyes and began to sing a Gregorian chant in a light baritone voice.

I was immediately transported back to my childhood, back in the little bluestone St John's church in Heidelberg at the masses, benedictions and ritual ceremonies that made up a large part of my childhood. I could smell the incense, I could see the light reflecting from the beautiful and elaborate gold monstrance and chalices on the altar, and the stained-glass window behind the altar as light streamed through it. My childhood memories of religion are about a punishing God but I loved the old bluestone church with the smells and the music, and these memories are still strong and evocative. I learned these chants as a child. Often my dad and I would sing the benediction hymns together up in the organ gallery of the church, the only ones singing but somehow not self-conscious. Standing there beside my dad gave me courage. I had no idea what the words I was singing meant at the time and while the Latin has faded these chants are still deeply familiar.

We moved on to portraits in the next room. As I moved from one to another, looking at the faces of famous and infamous people, I started to hear the sound of a deep flute. Years later I discovered that it was a Native American courting flute. Peter told me that it was a gift from a flute maker in the United States, handmade for Peter's needs in a particular key. Peter had sent him a didgeridoo in thanks.

Now, here in the gallery, haunting in its plaintive call, the sound moved slowly up an octave, a small trill, and down, dying away at the end. The tune repeated, shifted and changed, but always with this fading away at the end. It was like a wail, a lament, a sad call that was never answered. People stood around, some with eyes closed, others gazing unseeingly at walls or the ceiling as they listened. The last fading end disappeared into the air and there was stillness and silence. Peter had gone.

Yet another room. Here there were more pictures and central cabinets holding small sculptures and miniatures. We milled around looking at the artwork, but waiting for the next musical instalment. Peter was standing by a cabinet with his eyes shut and his hands clasped together as if in prayer. His head tilted back and he started to sing an Islamic call to prayer. I left the cabinets and watched. His face strained with concentration. His throat quivered and shook as his vocal chords and facial muscles produced the dramatic musical sounds.

I have never been to the Middle East but I knew this music from the in-flight CDs on Qatar Airlines. I once played Abdel Halim Hafez over and over on a long-haul flight to London.

I listened entranced when the host of *Weekend Planet* on Radio National presented a track called 'Intimate Dialogue' by 'Azerbaijan's living vocal treasure' Alim Qasomov and his daughter Fergana. Later I Googled them and watched a DVD, mesmerised by Fergana's face and her deep concentration as she sang with her father. I bookmarked it and watch it often. I have never lost the way it leaves me breathless.

Some of my friends have lived and nursed in the Middle East and I knew that they had eventually found the call to prayer intrusive and irritating. I could not imagine ever tiring of these intricate and complex sounds.

Anne turned to me. 'This is amazing,' she said. 'It's wonderful.'

I agreed.

The last room, this time a large space with a huge round leadlight window that was behind Peter. Light filtered through this window.

Anne laughed softly and whispered, 'It's like an aura. Wonder if he planned that.'

This room had black leather seats in the centre and I sat on one of those. There was some chatter amongst the group and the start of a little restlessness. But then he started. What came from his throat was a long, low drone. Almost like a growl. It changed, becoming lighter, smoother, and I paid attention to his breathing for a while because it was strange, almost as if he was not breathing at all for long periods. And then I could hear it. The hairs on my neck stood up and I shivered. Over this low drone, there was a second, simultaneous sound. It was a clear, sweet, pure soprano soaring. This second note rose and fell while the drone stayed constant.

The woman beside me turned and said, 'How does he do that?'

I could not reply. I swallowed the lump in my throat, conscious of the tear tracking to my jaw and falling onto my shirt. This went on and on and there was total silence in the room. Everyone was totally focused on the sounds. When it ended, the silence continued. No one wanted to break the spell.

One day, after we had become friends, Peter told me the story of how he came to learn about this music. It started with an LP recording that he borrowed from a library. Thinking the sound fascinating, he wanted to know more. Someone mentioned a sound recordist in Melbourne who knew how to sing in this way, so Peter tracked him down and went to visit. Andrew, the man he had come to see, lived in a bungalow in someone's backyard. A single room, the bungalow was full of speakers, sound equipment and albums. The only furniture that Peter remembers was a rolled-up futon in a corner. This was a serious lover of music.

The bungalow nestled in a large native garden full of eucalypt trees and shrubs. Andrew appeared barefooted and casually dressed. He greeted Peter with a hug. In his work clothes, neat slacks and colour-coordinated tie and shirt, Peter wished he had dressed differently, feeling that his exterior would paint him as worlds apart from this man and his environment.

Andrew made herbal tea and they chatted about the various things in the room that encapsulated his work and interests. The albums were all unusual and exotic. Peter saw that Andrew had the same album he had borrowed from the library

'So you're interested in harmonic singing,' Andrew said. 'Would you like me to sing for you?'

Andrew knelt on the floor. Peter knelt too so they faced each other. When he reflected on the kneeling position, Peter was not sure whether it was a sign of reverence for this sound, or simply a lack of chairs. Andrew began to sing. Peter closed his eyes and let this music wash over him. It took very little time for the music to affect him profoundly. He felt tears running down his cheeks. 'I was falling apart,' he told me. 'It was exquisite.'

After a while, Peter left Andrew's home. He drove a little way and then stopped the car and tried to reproduce the sounds he had heard. And he could. With no training, no explanation, he could do it. 'I think it's something I heard,' he told me. 'I had my eyes closed so I wasn't watching what he did. I was simply letting it flow over me, but I could hear something that I think told me how to do it.'

Harmonic singing, or Mongolian overtone singing, as he sometimes calls it, transports Peter. He feels that it is a direct expression of something deep and mysterious. It is something that he knows he could do anywhere, at any time, but he chooses not to. For him it is not a party trick; he is respectful about when and where he sings in this way. He suspects that kneeling signified this respect in Andrew as well.

Back to the gallery. Slowly we filtered back out into the foyer. Peter was greeting people, being introduced to others and smiling his thanks at compliments. People had enjoyed the morning. Many were asking him about the harmonic singing that was his final musical offering, never having heard it before and asking how he managed those dual sounds. I waited until people were moving away and walked forward and introduced myself. He was surprised. We shook hands. I told him that I had enjoyed his performance very much. I still had tears in my eyes from the final piece and could not really manage conversation. He said that he was pleased I came. We arranged to meet for coffee to plan the start of my work with the study.

Over the next eighteen months we would work together on the Kings research project, he offering vigils, me watching, recording, speaking to people about it. It was a profound experience for me. Somewhere in that time Sarah Leach resigned from

Deakin University and so her part in the study ended. I took over leadership of the project. I wrote a detailed report for Kings Australia, Deakin University and the St John of God Hospital.

Amongst a great deal of data, I singled out two people as 'case studies' because they epitomised for me the power of what it is that Peter does. The next two chapters will introduce you to these two people, Alice and Robert, and tell their stories.

3

B

Alice: Taking the Knots Out

As we had arranged at the gallery concert, Peter and I met in Costa's, the St John of God Hospital coffee shop. All these years later, Costa's is still where we meet most frequently. Peter spent an hour or so telling me more about music-thanatology, how he came to it, and the kind of training he had in the United States of America. I knew I needed to understand a great deal more, but I decided to attend a vigil with Peter, where he would play at the bedside of someone who was dying, before talking further so my questions could be informed. We planned a date for me to join him at the hospital.

For my first vigil as the researcher for the Kings study, I dressed soberly in black wool trousers, quiet-soled black shoes, a claret-red shirt and a black silk jacket that had deep red threads through it. I had a satchel with the forms that I would complete for each person in the study and each vigil, a clipboard to rest them on and some pens. I wanted to look professional but invisible, to fade into the background so as not to interfere with what Peter was doing or the relationship he had with Alice, the woman we were to visit.

I arrived at the hospital early, called Peter on my mobile to let him know I was there, and he directed me to the pastoral-services unit where he would be waiting for me. Once there, he introduced me to the team. They had just concluded a meeting. Clearly they knew who I was; Peter had told them about my role in the research. They smiled a warm welcome and offered me a cup of tea, which I accepted so I could sit a while with these women. After ten minutes of chatting we decided that perhaps we should all get on with work.

Peter and I set off for the ward. We walked down a long corridor, with rooms on either side. Some were single rooms; others had two or more beds. A nurses' station was at the junction of two corridors and there were utility rooms that held all of the things you would expect: medicines, lotions and sterile equipment in one, bedpans, urinals and a sluice in another. There was an odour, one of those deodorisers used to mask more unpleasant odours. As a nurse this was all deeply familiar to me.

Peter checked in with the nurse caring for Alice, asking if it was okay to play the harp for her.

The nurse snapped, 'Play for her! I would like to wrap the harp around her head.' She had had enough of Alice's constant demands, she told us. A moment later, however, she said that the music could be helpful to Alice, perhaps calm her, and then she headed off to answer yet another call bell.

We looked at each other.

'Hmm,' I murmured. 'This might not be smooth sailing.'

Alice was resting on top of the bedcovers. At eighty-two years of age she looked thin and pale. Her eyes were sunken with deep shadows underneath. She wore a blue nightdress with a burgundy dressing gown over the top. Her feet were bare. Her white hair was drawn back behind a headband. Her tired eyes lit up as Peter entered the room; it was clear from her smile that she knew who he was, and he was welcome. Peter had played for her a number of times before. She reached out to him and Peter took her bony hand with its thin parchment skin just for a moment.

He placed a chair and his harp to the right of her bed, up close so he could clearly watch her, and another further back, for me. He knew I needed to be where I could watch both Alice and Peter because I wanted to note not only her reactions, but also any changes in what Peter did. He stuck a notice on the outside of the door asking people not to enter unless necessary. He shut the door and started to play.

Alice was a musician herself and so she drifted into the music, smiling, eyes shut. It was a peaceful, uneventful vigil. Not all of the vigils with Alice would be like this.

After the vigil we drove away in the car and found somewhere for coffee; this time down by the water at Eastern Beach. We talked about Alice and what I had written. Peter wanted to know how I experienced the vigil. I wanted to know how he experienced my presence. I thought back on my role at the vigil. Conscious of needing to be completely silent, I had used single sheets of paper to avoid rustling and made sure my pen made no scratching noise. I had worked hard to have Peter not be distracted by my presence. We made plans to visit Alice again.

There is no particular timing to vigils. They may occur twice or three times in a single day if the person is close to death and is in the hospital where Peter is employed, as Alice was in the beginning. They may occur weekly, or every second week, or even monthly if the person is at home or in a nursing home;

environments where Peter needs to plan a special trip. Sometimes he will go only if a relative calls and invites him.

I once witnessed Peter give a dying man his business card and tell him that he could call at any time, and that he would be pleased to come and play for him even at night or on the weekend if he thought it would help him.

This man held out the card to his wife as she entered the room. 'Look love,' he said, 'it's Peter's card with his telephone number.' He chuckled, 'Peter's going to play me out.'

I knew his wife had been in the garden of the hospital having a quiet weep. She smiled wanly at his humour, but her tears were close. His going was perhaps not high on *her* agenda, but he was ready.

Before the second vigil with Alice commenced, I asked her how she had experienced the first one. She said it was beautiful but that she 'wouldn't want to go too deeply into it'. I knew she meant not letting go, losing control. She told me that she knew she was dying, but she was scared. She said that if she didn't go too deeply into the music, she might be able to delay the dying. Being a musician gave her a way of keeping control. She concentrated on the key, the notes and the tempo, and whatever else kept her mind active and focused.

I wished that I could find the words to help her, to encourage her not to fight against what this music could do for her. She had to find that for herself.

After her symptoms were treated, Alice returned to her nursing home and we continued to visit her there for some six months. Sometimes she was hot and distressed before we arrived and would strip off her clothes as Peter was starting a vigil. She would sit with just a singlet covering her sunken chest. Sometimes even the singlet became unbearable. Such things never distracted Peter; he would persevere, offering her calm, soothing music until she settled. I would take it on myself to find something light to cover her and to sit by the door guarding her. Sometimes I failed, though, and a resident would slip into the room after Peter had started playing, like an eager concert audience. If they were quiet and Alice was calm I would let them be. They were Alice's friends.

In another conversation with Alice a couple of months into our visits with her, she told me that she felt she was 'winding down'. Being a nurse, I could tell from her laboured breathing and the sweaty sheen on her skin that she had moved from being uncomfortable to being sicker, in more pain as her cancer spread. She had been hopeful she would improve but now she could see there was really no hope for improvement and that she was dying. She didn't want any more treatment; she really wanted to die, but she was scared. The music-thanatology vigils were helping her, though, she said. The music soothed her and helped her to feel more comfortable both in her body and in her mind. It seemed that she had stopped focusing on the technical aspects of the music and was now moving into quiet space as Peter played. She told me that 'the music takes the knots out'.

In a vigil just a couple of months before she died, Alice described feeling ecstatic. She said the music took her to another place. She called it heaven and said it was filled with flowers. This was different to just having her mind taken off her struggles. From then on, she went to this other world at every vigil. I had heard other people describe this reaction to a vigil and I was thankful that Alice had found this place too.

On the second to last vigil, she said she could feel light streaming out her fingers as she left for this other place; there was a tingling and she just went into it. She described this as another form of healing – not one that would cure her, but better than all the pills.

I told Peter what she had said and he was touched and grateful. The work of the music-thanatologist is lonely; there is seldom any feedback. He plays until someone is peaceful and then he quietly leaves the room, trying not to disturb the serenity he has worked to create.

One of the joys of this research for Peter was that he heard for the first time how deeply helpful what he does is to people who are dying.

On the final vigil Alice wondered aloud whether she could let go and surrender to the music. She wondered if she could just go into the music and not return. She said that would be a beautiful way to die. She died just a couple of days later.

Over the months we spent together she eventually reached a state where she was ready to die, had deeply accepted it, and was impatient. It took around three months from when Alice decided she was ready to die until she actually did die, and in all that time she constantly said, 'Why doesn't He take me now?' She said that it felt her waiting to go would never end. She was not in pain; by then she was medicated for pain. Her lingering sense was of deep tiredness. It seemed to me that this dying was hard work for her until she found the place of serenity.

4

ℛ

Robert: The Place of No Fear

R obert was stretched out on the dark-red and gold sofa, lying on his back with his eyes closed. A deep-red, woollen dressing gown allowed glimpses of blue and white striped flannelette pyjamas at his neck and legs. His feet were thrust into brown scuffed slippers. At the foot of the sofa Peter played the harp, not the usual place he would sit when playing for someone but this vigil had morphed spontaneously from something else. I was at Robert's side with a notepad and pen in my hand, and over my right shoulder a video cameraman and a sound recordist were working.

Robert had been a participant in our Kings research project for over a year. Now, for two hours, I had been interviewing him about his illness, his approaching death and the ways that Peter and the harp music had helped him. He had put up a strong fight for survival but he was declining. I knew that his experience of music-thanatology had been profound, having been witness to it, and it had been for me as well, but now, hearing his words, his experience had been even more profound than I realised.

This was August 2006. Peter and I had been invited to the United States in October and November to present the findings of our research. The Providence St Vincent Organisation was sponsoring us as keynote speakers at their conference, 'Spiritual Care: An Essential Component in Patient Care'. In addition, we were presenting at the Music-Thanatology Association International (MTAI) annual conference, 'Spreading Our wings: Research and Education Emerge', in Portland, Oregon; at the 'Life Near the End of Life' conference at the Mayo Clinic in Minnesota; and I was to give a paper we had titled 'Reflections and Insights: The Australian Music-thanatology Research Project' at a gathering of academic staff and research students at the University of British Columbia in Canada.

It would be a full-on speaking tour and we were looking forward to it. I had asked Robert if he felt up to this interview because a message from him would be affirming to those at the Oregon conference of music-thanatologists. He responded with delight.

Now the interview had ended. Peter was playing from where he had been sitting listening to the interview. The film crew were at work capturing the vigil that we would use to end the tape. Robert rested. Even though he had wanted to do the interview, it had been taxing.

Peter played a tune I had heard many times before and I closed my eyes for a moment to listen. Then – a sudden discordant moment. I recognised something else about the music. It was the soundtrack behind a game of solitaire on my computer. I play that card game when my writing gets stuck. Shaken out of the vigil moment by this image, I felt uncomfortable; it seemed a bit irreverent. I felt embarrassed and wondered if my distraction showed.

A moment later, I noticed that the harp was casting a shadow on the wall and without watching Peter I could follow his movements in the shadow, his hands, his fingers moving over the strings, picking out the notes. I watched this shadow play and that previous discordant moment faded. I hoped the cameraman had noticed the shadow, but I didn't alert him. The moment was so fine. I felt like it should not be disturbed. I sat and watched.

The music played on softly and Robert slept. The cameraman was now filming from the window. Robert's home overlooks Corio Bay and there was a stunning red and gold sunset over the water. Later, when we saw the finished product, we found that the cameraman had used the shadow play of harp and fingers on the wall with the sunset over the water. The music played as the sun dipped lower until finally we were left in darkness and the music ended. It was hauntingly beautiful in both vision and sound, but the metaphor of Robert's life ebbing away was unmistakeable, and in the darkness we wiped our tears.

At eighty-three years of age Robert was a tall and charismatic man. He had been a prominent public speaker all his adult life. He had had surgery around a year before we met him and at that time he developed a septicaemia for which he required several courses of antibiotics. Doctors assumed that the serious infection, coupled with the type of antibiotics he needed, depleted his immune system, which then resulted in rapid proliferation of cancer in his lungs.

The specialist told Robert that he had probably only around three months to live. He decided to have chemotherapy because the specialist said that although it might only give him another month or so it would make him more comfortable. The Pastoral Services staff visited him in the ward and he spoke to them at great length about his life, his rejection of his prognosis and his determination to beat this cancer. Peter played for him not because he had a terminal illness, but because Robert needed resources to maintain his hope and strength. He agreed to enter our research program because after experiencing Peter's music he felt he had a new task. He needed to tell the world in general, and the medical world in particular, about this music and what it did for people who had been given no hope. He believed that this task would be the thing that kept him alive.

Peter played six vigils with Robert in my presence. In reality, he played many more. The vigils commenced in the hospital and continued after Robert had gone home. The vigils I observed were extraordinary because Robert was able to describe in great detail what was happening to him.

When I met Robert, he told me that the gap between medicine and what comes next was the most painful thing for him. He railed at medicine because he felt it had failed him. 'Medicine remains unfinished while they don't heal in the true sense,' he said.

He meant that medicine could offer him no cure, but neither was there any attempt to offer him any healing, some way to live well with whatever time remained, and to prepare for death with grace. This resonated with my experiences as a nurse in the acute-care system. Death as failure. The real failure, though, is not about curing the illness, but the failure to really help people who are dying,

In the beginning Robert liked the music because he found it beautiful, peaceful and relaxing. Over time his experience of the vigils changed. After the first vigil, he said that it was 'complete and exactly' what he needed. He had started having massage and doing meditation but the music brought it all together and that is what he meant by complete.

On the second vigil, he said that it took him to a place of relaxation, where he could remove himself from thinking. From then on, however, the experience became deeper and more profound. He told me that he went to another place altogether, not just a place of calm but somewhere where he could look down on the world as it is going to be. He experienced love and trust. He called it 'the haven; the place of no fear'.

On the sixth vigil, Robert reported that he had had a very bad night. He had drenched his pyjamas with sweat, had been coughing blood, sores had developed on his face and he had been in a panic. He started to organise his wife to phone a doctor or get an ambulance and then he stopped. He wondered if he could take himself to 'the haven' where the music usually took him . . . and he did. He was delighted that he had conquered his panic and had become calm and peaceful. When we arrived, he was almost euphoric.

I found this encounter with such a powerful response illuminating. I knew that we were fortunate that these people had agreed to be in the study and so I was able to hear these stories. Without the research we would not have understood the change that occurred with multiple vigils. It is easy to feel humbled by being part of this, even in a small way.

In the car on the way back, Peter said, 'My work is done. When someone moves from music to silence, there's no further need for me and what I do.'

For Robert, the music took him where he needed to go. The music showed him the way but now he could go there by himself, and, like Alice, this was the place from where he could die, peacefully. That was the 'aha' moment for me, the moment when I really *got* music-thanatology. I understood what it was all about. Yes, it is music that comforts, that brings peace that eases pain and distress, but the real intention of music-thanatology is about helping people to stop the struggle and to let go. It is described as helping with 'unbinding and leave-taking' and that is exactly what it is, and it is exactly right.

It was through Alice, and Robert in particular, that I decided to make a commitment to this work, to try to help it survive and grow in Australia. Our research would help but that would be just a start.

At the MTAI conference in Portland, Oregon, we showed Robert's film and in a candlelit ritual we gave everyone present a copy of our research report. They were deeply moved by the entire presentation. Peter had the assembled music-thanatologists record messages to Robert in a beautifully bound book he had brought with him. Each person wrote a heartfelt message and before we moved on to the next conference, Peter mailed it to him back home in Australia with our love.

Sadly, Robert died before Peter and I returned from the speaking tour. And he died before our package reached him. We were both saddened, but we would not have wished for him to hold on, waiting for our return. We knew he was ready. His family read out several of the messages from the book at the funeral service and they were deeply moved to have received it. The family had seen the film we made, and have a copy of it. They regretted that Peter had not been present to play for Robert in those dying moments. They knew that the music he offered had been so helpful. Peter and I hoped he had died from the space that he had found: the haven.

The results of the Kings Australia project were presented at a well-attended function at St John of God Hospital. The report was welcomed as a positive example of the care that they offer to terminally ill people. Peter was moved from a contract position to a permanent part-time member of staff, a sure sign that he was, and is, respected and valued. I hope that our report contributed to that decision. If so, it was another wonderful outcome.

5

Ɓ'

Just Play Me Away

Through the encouragement and advice of a generous donor to his work, Peter established the Institute of Music in Medicine (IMIM), a non-profit charity that enabled him to apply for grants to offer the music-thanatology service outside the St John of God Hospital. When I was invited to become one of the directors of the institute, I took it upon myself to be the grant writer and we were successful a number of times. The Tattersall's Foundation was generous, as was the Geelong branch of United Way, now known as Give Where You Live. Each grant required a report and so I undertook these tasks.

Through United Way, the Glover Foundation funded an extension of the music-thanatology service into the Barwon Health McKellar palliative-care unit, Anam Cara Community Hospice and some outlying nursing homes. The evaluation of that service was our second study in palliative care and the results confirmed what we had found in the first one: that people who are dying are helped by the live harp music and, as many of them told me, by Peter's presence.

For part of this evaluation I asked people to self-rate their level of calmness, peacefulness, tiredness, worry, distress and optimism before and after the music was played, and found statistically significant changes for the better in all categories. People were calmer, more peaceful, less distressed and so on. The results were not surprising; they simply validated what we were being told and what we could observe everywhere we went.

This is not to say that every person welcomed Peter and his music. Some were uncomfortable with the idea. They associated harp music with angels and death and they were sometimes vehement that they were 'not ready for that yet'. Sometimes that 'not being ready' continued right to death. Sometimes, while people with the illness welcomed Peter relatives felt they had to leave the room because he represented the reality of what was happening, which they were rejecting. Peter would always ask if they would like the music and just leave if they said no. He was always available to people who connected with it and found it helpful.

Sometimes people surprised themselves, rejecting the music and then, hearing it somewhere else in the ward, changed their minds. Many of those people had profound experiences, like those of Alice and Robert, once they had opened themselves to the possibility that it could help them.

During my evaluation work, I observed that in most cases, patients and relatives knew Peter. He had played for all of them before, some at the hospital where they had been before they had been transferred to palliative care, some at the McKellar Centre at times when I was not present.

At the very first vigil that I attended for this second study, the elderly patient smiled delightedly when Peter entered the room. He reminded Peter that he had played for him at St John of

God. His comment as we entered the room was 'Ah, dream time!' He immediately adjusted his bed to recumbent, laid back and closed his eyes with a little smile on his face.

Another who had also experienced vigils before welcomed Peter. He told Peter he felt he was slipping and then added, 'You should expect that.' He said he had 'passed the three score years and ten at the age of eighty-nine, well past the allocation'. He was ready. His only fear was of pain; he wanted to have pain well managed.

He was one of many people to be captivated by the reverie harp, a new instrument that Peter co-designed and uses in the hospitals sometimes. The reverie harp is an oval-shaped, flat instrument that someone who is sick in bed can lay across the chest and play. The strings of the harp are tuned to a specific scale that is calming. It is strung differently from other string instruments in that the bass notes are in the centre and the higher notes fan out towards the outer edges. The notes are offset so that playing from the centre out can create harmony. Anyone can play it and make beautiful sounds.

The genesis of the reverie harp is a story worth telling. One day Peter played for a terminally ill patient suffering from multiple sclerosis. In conversation afterwards the man told Peter that he played a small harp too. Peter was curious and asked if someone could bring it into the hospital the next time they met so they could play something together.

It turned out to be a small and very basic homemade instrument; just a shaped soundbox with a dozen or so wire strings set across it. It certainly wasn't a harp but Peter could see by the way the man unwrapped it from its scarf covering that it was well loved. Several of the strings were out of tune so Peter retuned them, but the man's severely shaking finger wasn't able to pluck the strings in order to play music of any sort. Peter told me how touching and sad it was to see him trying so hard in his attempts to play music on his 'harp'.

This encounter set Peter thinking and over the next few months he began to think about creating an instrument that someone like this man could play, something that would be simple to use, comforting to hold and one that would produce beautiful sounds right away.

'I wanted to create an instrument for the patient, not the therapist,' he told me. He wanted to make an instrument that by virtue of its tuning would sound instantly uplifting and soothing when strummed, one that looked beautiful and felt comforting to hold in order to bring comfort and pleasure even if it wasn't played. He also needed it to be small enough to play while lying in bed and could be felt vibrating on the body when it was strummed. Peter didn't like the idea of having any cut string ends protruding to prick unwary fingers either.

On a trip to the United States Peter shared his ideas with Jerry Brown, a friend and musical-instrument maker. Over the ensuing months an instrument was created, Peter contributing from his experience as a therapeutic musician, his friend from his skill in musical instrument design and construction.

Peter came up with the name reverie harp from the instrument's ability to bring the player into a pleasant state of reverie, or daydream.

The man in our study stroked the reverie harp gently while Peter played.

People reacted variously to the vigils. Generally they remained resting quietly into the music, but some wanted to comment on a particular piece, and some even sang along if they had asked Peter to play a particular favourite tune. One woman sang valiantly even when she was struggling to breathe. Others went to sleep. One woman who was not conscious and who had very laboured breathing seemed to adjust her breath to what Peter was doing. In particular, whenever he paused she would stop breathing, as if hushed, listening for the music to return. She did not otherwise rouse at all. Some people clearly went into another 'space', the kind of place that seems not of this earth, and that I have mentioned previously.

At the end of some fifteen minutes of playing, one man opened his eyes and said, 'That was magnificent; I could get up and fly away. Thank you, I just came back down to earth again.'

Peter tried to encourage this man to stay with this feeling while he played. 'It's good to listen with your mind,' he said, 'but it's also good to just drift away and not to feel you need to make any comment, just stay with it.' Peter told him that he was always happy to just creep out of the room and did not ever need thanks or even any comment.

The work of creating the quiet 'other' space is what it is all about. Interestingly, people who found this place to go to in their minds were never aware of distractions around them. There were instances of food-service staff members entering a room noisily, of construction workers hammering and making other loud noises outside a window, of noisy discussion in corridors, telephones ringing – all the noise you would associate with such an environment – and patients saying they had not heard it.

A woman who met Peter for the first time on a day I was present watched with a small smile on her face the whole time. She did not close her eyes; her breathing was even and peaceful. When he finished one tune she said, 'It's beautiful, it's like a lovely meditation. You must get such joy from this work.'

Peter talked with her about finding that quiet place from where troubles are removed. Her response was: 'What a wonderful thing to be doing in a place like this, where people don't know if they're going home or not.'

This woman also delighted in her discovery of the reverie harp and Peter returned at a later time to give her some lessons. I did not return for further vigils with her, but had reports from Peter about how important the reverie harp became for her. She used it as she became sicker, to calm herself and manage her fear.

The four vigils I attended for one elderly woman were particularly beautiful. She had her son and daughter-in-law with her every time I went there. Sometimes she also had a special group of friends she called her 'three amigos'. She was close to death and these people were devoted to her, staying in what I think of as the first deeply spiritual vigil to death that I have ever witnessed. I envied them their closeness in this dying time and wished that I had provided this for people close to me who have died.

She was frail, but kept a dignity – almost holding court from her bed. In fact, one day when I arrived she had a scarf on her head and over the scarf, a tiara. Wearing makeup and pearls, she was indeed holding court. From then on she was labelled 'Her Maj'. At first she talked, but over time she became too tired, in the end acknowledging Peter with eyes that swam into focus very briefly.

She always inclined her head toward the harp. After the first vigil I witnessed, she said, 'Thank you, that was beautiful. I really could go to sleep and go to heaven. It was so tranquil. I wish you could just play me away.'

Everyone in the room wanted exactly that for her, including me – that she could use this beautiful experience of music to transcend life forever. It is impossible to be a distanced observer in these research studies.

℘

It seemed to me that Peter was an accepted member of this sacred space, but that he shaped it a little differently. The space was there when he entered, but the music changed it a little, deepened it, moved it away from grief and loss to something else. People emerged calmer, softer, and more peaceful, the very thing all had indicated they were looking for.

In my conversations with patients, they told me things like 'I feel very connected to my emotions and much calmer when he plays' or 'the weight lifted from my shoulders' or 'I felt peaceful and even managed some sleep'. One woman told me that it soothed her jangled thoughts.

When I asked if there were any final comments they wanted to make about the experience, one said, 'The atmosphere of the room seemed to change. It was as though a cloud of peace and calmness was hovering. '

'The music always centres me,' another said. 'It makes me feel less anxious, depressed and worried. It's almost a spiritual experience and certainly very comforting.'

Relatives too found solace. From the self-rating surveys I did with them, I found positive results in all categories except tired and frightened. There was some improvement in those two, but not to statistical significance. This is not surprising. Relatives were keeping long and exhausting vigil at the bedside and they knew that the outcome of their wait was going to be loss and grief. Relatives expressed mixed reactions to the music. Some indicated that they loved it, that they could see how much their relative loved it too and they were delighted that this pleasure was available at such a difficult time. Others cried softly, sometimes trying to hide the tears from the person dying. They expressed sadness and grief at the impending death of someone they loved and didn't want to lose. Sometimes this was letting go of pent-up and unexpressed emotion. Sometimes it was the tired crying of acceptance.

I asked relatives what they would like from the vigil for their loved one who was dying. They generally responded with words like peace, calmness, and acceptance. When I asked them what they would like for themselves, they used words and phrases like 'just a moment to be', 'take my mind from the problems for a while' and 'just to see him smile'. They told me they were grieving, exhausted and finding it hard to think.

After the music one person said, 'It was wonderful to share it with my mother, another precious moment.'

Another said, 'The pressure in the front of my head, which I didn't know was there, has gone.'

Final comments from a daughter were, 'It was unexpectedly moving and beautiful. Although Mum cried, it was obvious that she enjoyed and appreciated the experience.'

In the conclusion of the report to United Way I wrote:

The findings of this small study indicate that patients and relatives alike derive comfort from music-thanatology. Greater than comfort, though, is the way in which music-thanatology links the music and the musician with those experiencing the vigil in a space that becomes altered. Patients and relatives alike become calmer and more peaceful, to some degree fear and distress abate, and for some patients, in particular those who experience multiple vigils, the possibility of finding a still, peaceful, core space is heightened. This is the space that Peter Roberts calls 'music into silence', when his work is done. It is the core purpose of music-thanatology, helping people to find that place of no fear or struggle, from which they can let go.

℘

In this study, some people seemed to know this space. The man who lay back and said, 'Ah, dream time,' in anticipation of the journey he would travel toward peace with the music was one; the man who said he had been flying was another. Relatives come to know this space also. They watched as their loved one sank into peacefulness and they willed with all their hearts that they would just let go into the music forever.

It is hard to imagine that anyone would want anything other than a 'good' death. In the studies that we have done, we have discovered over and over that people do not fear death. They fear the manner of dying. The notion of a less-than-good death is what we fear, that we may find ourselves in a busy place, with stressed health professionals who, with the best intentions in the world, are not able to offer what we need. The process of unbinding and leave-taking from all that we know and love, staring death in the face and finding a way to be ready, requires more than managing pain, nausea and the like. It requires an acknowledgement of the existential struggles too. It requires having people who are not afraid, who can walk the journey alongside them. Compassionate nursing and medical staff, and other health professionals do that simply by who they are and what they bring of themselves to what they do. Pastoral-services staff have this as intent. Music-thanatologists have this as intent also, and it makes an important contribution to dying well.

When the United Way grant finished Peter completed his work at Barwon Health. Then he was offered employment there on a contract for one day per week. At first it was sporadic contracts for months at a time. Now he has a second full-year contract and we are assured that the work there will continue into the future. Once again, we would like to think that the positive results of our research helped the decision-makers. If the study influenced them that would be a wonderful outcome, but whether it did or did not is irrelevant. It is not easy for public health services to stretch their budgets to services like music-thanatology when there are such pressures for acute-care services, equipment and staffing. It is testament to the ethos of the palliative-care team and the hospital executive that attention to the existential issues that surround dying are seen as just as important as attention to the physical symptoms that accompany a dying process.

6

B

The Full Circle

I walked into the St John of God Hospital at lunchtime on a Wednesday to meet with staff in the Special Care Nursery. We were to discuss the premature-baby project that had been funded by the Annie Danks Foundation. As I made my way through the third-floor corridors I heard the sound of a harp. I stopped to listen, trying to detect where it was coming from. Peter must be behind one of those doors, I thought. Then it stopped, and a few seconds later it repeated, just a small phrase from 'Brahms' Lullaby'.

Some nurses walking along chatting also stopped to listen. 'Ah,' said the tall dark-haired nurse, smiling. 'Two, how gorgeous.' And they walked on.

When I got to the nursery Peter was waiting for me. Surprised, I said, 'I thought you were in one of the rooms, I thought I just heard you playing.'

He smiled. 'That was the birthing unit. Haven't you heard it before?'

Then I remembered. Peter had told me that he had recorded himself playing 'Brahms' Lullaby' and that whenever a baby is born in the labour ward the midwife presses a button and the music floods throughout the hospital. In all the time I had been going to this hospital I had never heard it.

I recalled Peter telling me that when he was visiting Oregon in 2004 he came upon a hospital with this practice of playing music to welcome a newborn baby into the world. Sister Vivian Ripp, one of his music-thanatologist friends, had instigated it in the hospital where she worked. He thought it was so beautiful to hear this music and understand what it meant that he took the idea to the executive at St John of God on his return. There were technicalities and costs and ethical considerations to consider. Eventually all the issues were worked through and the executive agreed to implement it. And I had just heard it flooding over the hospital intercom.

I asked him why they played it twice.

He chuckled and said, 'Twins!'

Now the nurse's comment made sense. She was right. It was gorgeous.

Now I have heard it many times, and I watch other people when it plays. I see staff members pause for just a moment and smile. It is like there is a collective sigh across the hospital and the feeling is gentler, just for a moment.

When people discover the meaning behind the little tune that plays briefly but often, they are profoundly moved. Some have told me that it changes the way they think about this hospital. Mothers I have spoken to treasure the moment they heard the music announcing and welcoming their baby. Mothers whose babies did not survive see the music as a validation of their baby's life. That the music was still played for their little one was important. Often mothers ask Peter to play at the baby's funeral. He always plays 'Brahms' Lullaby' if they ask.

Our third study was to be with these newborn babies. It was a delightful project that studied the effects of Peter's music on babies in the Special Care Nursery. This is a unit for babies who are premature or unwell and is a second-level care unit, which means the babies are not sick enough to be in intensive care, but neither are they well enough to be roomed in with their mothers. They need careful surveillance and monitoring, and quick interventions should situations change, which they do, frequently and quite suddenly.

Over the years that Peter has played there the nurses in the special-care unit have often talked of seeing changes in the babies as he plays. Sometimes Peter and a nurse would catch each other's eye and smile as they both noticed a response that could only be due to the music.

The grant money had been earmarked for musical environments for children, so what better place than the Special Care Nursery where little ones were struggling to get a firm foothold on life. Peter thought it would be good to do a little project to check out the perception the nurses had about his music being helpful there. I worked with the unit manager, associate unit manager and other staff members in the nursery to design a small pilot study. We put it to the executive and the committee of management at the hospital and they approved it.

The evaluation project took place over 2009–10. I titled the report: 'The Use of Prescriptively Played Harp Music in the Special Care Nursery.' In this study I found more interesting information about the effects of music-thanatology.

Although this was not a palliative-care study, I use the term 'music-thanatology' because I discovered that Peter uses the principles he was taught for this skill in everything he does. I will return to the principles when I have described the study and my findings.

For this study I gathered information from the babies' behaviour and their monitors, from their parents, from the staff and from Peter. I also recorded my own observations.

I measured heart rate, blood-oxygen levels and behaviour on fifty-eight babies. In fact we had many more babies, but we had to eliminate dozens from the study when things happened during the observation period, like parents using flash photography that disturbed the baby and changed readings, or procedures like insertion of an intravenous line, or heel pricks were done.

All the babies in the study were attached to monitors and so, as the researcher, I did not have to do anything other than watch. I could see the heart rate and its rhythm on the screen, I could see the blood oxygen levels flashing up. For behaviour, I drew up a very simple chart, scoring 1 for babies who were asleep, 2 for babies who were awake but peaceful and contented, 3 for babies who were restless and agitated, and 4 for babies who were crying and distressed. I took measurements of heart rate, blood-oxygen levels and behaviour before the music started, every two minutes for the duration of the music, and again at two minutes after the music ended. This kind of research is called a simple pre-test–post-test study and is useful as a pilot study where such work has never been done before.

What I discovered was that once the music was being played, heart rates decreased in two-thirds of the babies, blood-oxygen levels increased in a similar number, and at least half of the babies who had been asleep woke up but were contented. I had no trouble deciding that they had woken and were listening. At the two-minute mark after the music ended, a little more than half of the babies still had a decreased heart rate and two-thirds still had increased blood-oxygen saturation levels. All of the babies were either asleep or awake but content: a lovely result.

As a nurse, I know that when any baby is born, their immediate task is to initiate breathing and to sustain the getting of air into previously fluid-filled lungs. Babies born at full term generally manage this well, but premature infants have more difficulty just because their lungs are not yet fully developed. The management of these babies in special-care nurseries includes the careful management of oxygen. Nurses keep blood-oxygen levels lower in premature babies since higher oxygen levels push up carbon dioxide levels when the babies have trouble getting rid of it. They become sicker. This little study showed, though, that these babies' oxygen levels were increasing because of some adaptive process within the babies themselves, some physiological process that occurred because of the music. Their oxygen levels went up and they became more stable, not more sick.

While we were present in the nursery, a number of unusual things happened. For example, we discovered that not all babies like the same music. Some don't like lullabies! Occasionally Peter would play a quiet lullaby and we would notice that a particular baby would become restless, moved about and grimaced. Peter would move to some other kind of music and the baby would settle immediately. He would test this by moving back and forth between the same lullaby and other music, and each time when he returned to the lullaby the same restless reaction occurred. This happened a number of times with different babies. One baby became restless with 'Brahms' Lullaby' but settled once Peter moved to a stronger, more rhythmic style of playing down in the lower-bass section of his harp. His amused mother remarked that she had been playing heavy-metal music throughout her pregnancy so she was not at all surprised to find her baby reacting negatively to lullabies.

On three different occasions in the nursery, and with three different babies, I was watching the blood-oxygen levels carefully while Peter played. In each instance the blood-oxygen levels rose: two from 91 to 100 and one from 94 to 99, and all remained steady through the music.

Then Peter decided to stop playing and gently stood the harp upright. As soon as the music stopped, in every instance the oxygen levels decreased steadily and swiftly: 99, 98, 97, 96, 95, 94 . . . The swiftness of the descent was so remarkable that Peter immediately began playing again, and immediately the blood-oxygen saturation levels went up: 94, 95, 96, 97, 98, 99 . . . as swiftly and steadily as they had gone down. There was no alteration to the babies' behaviour. They all appeared to be asleep. Again, we had no trouble concluding that the babies were holding their breath, listening for the music that had stopped.

On another occasion, a baby was drowsing in his mother's arms while she was sitting beside the crib. Peter played for some time and the baby was snuggled with his head on the mother's breast. It was peaceful and serene. After a time Peter stopped playing and immediately the baby lifted his head and turned toward Peter as if looking for where the sound had been and wanting it to come back. Peter played a little more and the baby settled back again.

On the second visit to this same baby the nurses commented that he was sensitive to noise. There were repairs going on in the nursery so a workman was hammering, and there was general busyness and loud voices. The nurses thought that since the baby had responded so positively the day Peter played for him they would locate the CD of Peter's music called *The Sanctuary* and play that. The baby became peaceful whenever they put it on. The CD was still playing when we arrived and the baby was asleep.

The mother commented that the CD was lovely, but 'she preferred the real thing'.

For the parents, I used the same self-rating scale that I have used over and over now. Using the same scale means that I can compare data across groups, though it does seem that this is hardly necessary. The results are always strongly positive. The analysis in this instance showed a statistically significant positive shift in every category except tiredness. More peaceful, less worried, for example.

I realised later that I had misinterpreted the tiredness category. These mothers had recently given birth, and their babies were unstable and unwell so the mothers were worried and not getting much sleep. The harp not only soothed them; it made them feel sleepy. Some told me that this sleepiness is what induced them to mark 'tired' as having increased on the measurement scale. Their response was to get into bed, pull up the covers and go into a deep restful sleep. This tiredness category that I was seeing in a negative way was qualitatively different from exhaustion for the mothers. They saw it as positive.

Comments from the parents related both to their child and to themselves. In respect of the baby, comments were: 'She was so much more relaxed and her breathing became deeper' and 'He was unsettled, but when the music started he settled and slept.' Several mentioned that although their baby was asleep, when the music started they turned their heads toward the sound.

For themselves, they found the music relaxing and soothing.

One mother said, 'It was so relaxing. To have my child sleep so soundly on my chest, listening to the music was great.'

'The music and the musician have an instant calming effect,' another mother said. 'Made me feel calmer, reflective, able to enjoy the moment with the babies [twins]. Makes my day every time.'

The clear benefit of the music for parents was the relaxing effect it had. Having sick and premature babies in the nursery is stressful. Some parents were frightened and not sure about the future for their babies, and even for those whose babies were not facing a life-threatening situation, seeing them undergoing invasive treatments was distressing. Mothers found the music helpful. They were also delighted at the effect that they could see the music had on their babies. They were grateful to Peter and to the nursery for having such a service.

This project was of deep interest to the nurses and they were keenly aware that it is rare to have an opportunity to obtain 'hard data' on sick babies without being intrusive, so babies already monitored created a unique opportunity to discover something about the effect of music. The nurses were not only interested in the wellbeing of the babies, though; they valued the music Peter offered for the ways in which it improved their day and their performance.

On a particularly busy and stressful day, one nurse said, 'We were having a terrible day, nine babies, one on a breathing machine waiting transfer, only two staff and then another baby starts to fit. We were sooo overstretched! Peter arrived with his harp amongst the mayhem. He found a corner and played. It was wonderful. Helped clear the head, slow the pulse, felt like we were being wrapped in a "blanket of soothing".'

As part of every study, I asked Peter to keep a journal of what he thinks about before he starts to play, why he chooses the music he does, what he is aiming for and what he observes as a music session, vigil or otherwise, proceeds. For every study

I analysed his journal. I have not described any of this in respect to the previous two studies, but what he wrote for this third study captures much of the others. In order to make sense of the earlier comment I made about music-thanatology principles, I will describe some of the analysis.

I found four key themes in Peter's notes: skilled assessment, offering comfort, impacting the environment, and music-thanatology principles. I will describe a little of each one to give a sense of his work. By the end the principles should be quite clear.

Skilled assessment captures the skill that goes into entering an environment and noticing what is happening there. Peter is able to quickly assess the state of the nursery: how many people are present, who they are and what they are doing, and to surmise from that where he needs to be and what he needs to do. His notes indicate that Peter often considers where he can locate himself so as to be unobtrusive, and to not add to the general clutter and chaos. Peter comments that he does not remember ever being directed by staff to a baby or a situation; it is always his own assessment that takes him to where he will play and why he should be there.

This skill in assessment also allows Peter to notice where attention is focused in the nursery, and to then decide whether there is a particularly sick baby or distressed parent who may benefit from having his music directed specifically to them. Even in quieter times, Peter is able to notice quiet tears from a distressed and worried mother and then approach her directly to talk softly and play for her. Skilled assessment is a feature of Peter's training and it is a skill he uses all day, every day.

Offering comfort has a great many notes and is perhaps one of the strongest. Peter works to give comfort to many: to unsettled and distressed babies, to babies having medical procedures, to tired mothers, to mothers struggling with breastfeeding for the first time, to fathers learning about newborn babies, to parents learning to bond with new babies.

He wrote about playing for a baby whose feeding tube had come out and the parents were distressed at the procedure to reinstate it. He wrote that he played in a gentle rhythmic way until the baby settled again and went to sleep.

He wrote about noticing a mother standing by her baby's isolette while treatment was being given. He noticed her wipe a tear and moved directly to her, speaking softly and offering his music. The mother held the baby while blood was taken. Peter played gently soothing music trying to hold a sense of calm. He wrote, 'The baby did not cry and neither did Mum!'

Another mother was upset that her baby was not feeding, but slept all the time. When Peter asked her if she thought her music was making him sleepy, she said, 'I don't know, but it's good for me,' indicating that she was comforted by it. Peter changed to a livelier tune and the mother rocked the baby to the rhythm. The baby took some more milk.

Another new mother was pale and tired after the birth of twins. Peter had played for her the day before also. 'I don't know about the babies,' she said, 'but it's doing me good,' almost a mantra amongst the mothers in the nursery. She took one of the twins for a bath and Peter played to support both of them. The bath was a calm event with neither mother nor baby becoming distressed. She was pleased.

A number of entries in Peter's notes showed how much he aims to impact the environment and how he is success-ful. The way he does this affects not only the babies there but the parents and staff members as well. I had many occasions where I witnessed the effect of Peter's presence and his music on the nursery in general.

On a typical busy day, we would arrive to find many people milling about: ambulance officers, doctors, parents, and many babies in cribs with alarms going off. The air would be tense and the faces of the nurses strained. Peter would sit quietly and unobtrusively, not playing for a particular baby in the first instance but playing to the room. After around ten minutes, I would notice the voices becoming a little less strident, a little quieter. Mothers would sit down and smile. After a few more moments it would become even quieter and the nurses' faces less strained. The mood of the nursery would change from being busy and stressed to being calm with a sense of people and things under control.

Once this happened, Peter would change where he was sitting and commence a vigil by moving to a particular baby, usually the one who was receiving the most attention, the sickest, the one everyone was most worried about. Everything was different.

Any wonder, when the study concluded, that one of the nurses said she was so sad. When I commented that it did not mean Peter would stop playing in the nursery she said, 'Yes, but this project guaranteed it!' They want him there all the time.

With regard to music-thanatology principles, as I have mentioned previously the music that Peter plays is not about playing 'nice' music to entertain or to create just a 'nice' experience. There is intention behind each vigil and behind everything that occurs within it. Peter's notes give many examples of the intention he forms before he commences playing. Peter wanted to comfort the baby who was having blood taken, and the one who was having the feeding tube inserted. He wanted to support a nervous father bathing his son for the first time. He wanted to calm a chaotic and stressed environment. He wanted to create a loving and caring space around a new mother bonding with her baby. He wanted to support and calm a stressed mother who was trying to breastfeed for the first time. All these are indications of the principle of intentionality, the first factor in the decision about what, how and why to play.

Then there are the decisions about how to proceed. As the music starts, Peter watches and observes things like agitation and laboured breathing, senses the mood of the room and the need of the person being played for, and then alters what he is doing accordingly. He might change the type of music, the rhythm or tempo. He might add or alter how he is using his voice. These are examples of the principle he calls 'prescriptive playing'. There was a specific example of this in the mother's comment about how one of her twin sons reacted to the use of voice by crying when it stopped and settling when it started again. The harp alone did not pacify this child.

Over and over Peter describes playing in a gentle rhythmic way to soothe unsettled babies. He describes how mothers rock their babies to the rhythm and the babies settle and sleep. He describes trying to play tenderly, reaching out to stressed parents. One baby was crying and the parents were both looking fragile. Peter played 'to instil calm with a gentle, simple melody that also had a slowly played supportive rhythm' and the baby settled.

There is one delightful anecdote in the notes about a father who asked Peter to play to his red-faced, loudly crying son. Peter did and the baby settled and stopped crying. The man was holding his son and rocking him, but not to the rhythm Peter was playing. Peter adjusted his rhythm to that of the father and wrote, 'I adjusted my tempo to his tango – everyone was happy!'

These principles – intentionality, the use of live harp and voice, the prescriptive nature of the music played – are all fundamental to music-thanatology and are what sets this apart from other forms of therapeutic music. In section 2, Peter will describe and illustrate these even further.

All of these studies have taught me a great deal about working with vulnerable, sick and terminally ill people. Over the years I have worked with Peter I have thought back to my own clinical nursing days and the kind of nurse I was, the kind of care I gave. I think about my nursing education and how it prepared me, or didn't, for the work in which I was engaged. I am aware, though, that I was a product of my times and my environment and the consciousness that prevailed then about death and dying. Times have changed perhaps. The very fact that people can train in courses like music-thanatology indicates that. I applaud the executives of the hospitals who value this contribution to patient care enough to employ Peter and I think that their willingness to allocate precious budget to it also indicates a different consciousness.

The story of Peter's work in the hospitals, however, does not stop with the findings of these studies. It is ongoing. He influences care in many varied ways. For example, sometime in 2010 Peter started talking with his colleagues in pastoral care about the fact that the hospital celebrates new life, but what about death? What about the people who die in the hospital? What about the friends and relatives who sit by them for long hours? What about the staff members who care for them, sometimes for a long time, only to have to prepare the newly vacated bed for someone else? Time does not stand still and there is always a new person in the bed where someone had lain for so long, being cared for by people to whom they mattered. What about them?

To acknowledge and give thanks for the life and death and the honour of caring for patients, the pastoral services team has devised rituals where they attend the room after the patient who died has been taken away. They gather any staff members who are free to attend, perhaps saying a prayer, perhaps reciting a poem: something that says goodbye, wishing the person who has died well on their ongoing journey, preparing the way for the next person and offering a prayer that everyone present will continue to recognise the dignity and value of each patient who is admitted to this room so they will feel the compassion and caring of the staff.

Peter had the idea, though, that more could be done to honour the life of the person who had died and he talked with his pastoral services colleagues about it. He was aware of lyrics entitled 'Going Home' that expressed a sense of leaving, slipping away. The words were set to a phrase from Dvořák's *9th Symphony*. Peter thought that this tune, played simply on the harp in the way that 'Brahms' Lullaby' was, would be perfect. He played it to them.

Having heard it, they understood and shared the feeling that it would be important. They kept returning to the conversation, mulling over the difficulties and the risks, and creating strategies to develop the idea.

There were times when people commented that they loved the little 'Brahms' Lullaby' tune and what it meant. Sometimes, if the moment felt right, the pastoral services staff member would say, 'Yes, it is lovely. You know, we've been wondering about whether we might do something like this when someone has just died, to honour their life and their presence in the hospital. What would you think about that?'

People would inevitably say, 'It would be lovely.' They stored those little comments away.

In 2011, the pastoral services coordinator worked for months with a family where the mother was dying. After she died, the coordinator stayed with the family while the funeral directors came to take her body away. They intended to escort her from the hospital with love and reverence. The woman's daughter was talking generally and mentioned the 'Brahms' Lullaby' ritual and how much they had enjoyed hearing the music as they kept vigil with their mother. As she had grown close to this woman, the coordinator felt it was an opportunity to tell her the new idea of playing when someone has died.

The daughter turned to her and said, 'I wish it was already in place now and that you could play it for Mum.'

The coordinator filed that away, too, another mental note. She continued her conversations with Peter on how they could help make this happen.

Together they worked on a presentation to the divisional management committee. When they were ready, they made an appointment through Trish Boom, the director of mission, to attend a management committee meeting to present their proposal. The immediate response of the committee members was that it was wonderful. They did not need convincing of the benefits and beauty of this planned ritual, and regardless of any financial implications they would do it as soon as practicable.

Peter and the coordinator were stunned. They had not expected this response to be so powerfully positive straight away.

There was a great deal to work through as the committee wondered how other patients who were dying would feel about this music being played. The feeling amongst the pastoral services team was that it could provide an ideal opportunity for patients to verbalise any concerns or fears they might have regarding their own mortality to a pastoral practitioner. There was also a need for appropriate education and preparation for caregivers for the project. A workshop was prepared and the team spent months visiting all areas of the hospital, showing their presentation, playing the music and allowing time for questions and feedback in general.

Some nurses were worried about the general patients, families and visitors and how they would react knowing that someone had just died. Others wanted to know how they could explain to people what the music was for, what words they could use. The pastoral-services team know only too well how hard people find talking about death. They were not surprised by this and were ready with solutions.

The message to be conveyed was about honouring someone's life. 'We've been caring for this person and their life has now come to an end. We want to honour them,' they suggested. The staff liked it. They liked the way it reflected their own feelings and the privilege some of them felt to have cared for someone in their last days.

A trial period was planned, but two weeks before the trial was to start Peter's colleague, one of the pastoral services team members, had a sister in the hospital who was close to death. He had played for her in the critical-care unit when his colleague was there. For the first time, now she was on the receiving end of what Peter called 'musical tender loving care'. The pastoral services member said that Peter's music brought 'a stillness'.

When Peter was not able to be present, they played his *Sanctuary* CD. The woman was not conscious but they felt that by movements of her hands she seemed to always know when Peter was there in person, playing. It was comforting to everyone.

On the day she died, Stephen Roberts, the chief executive of the hospital said, 'Let's begin right now.'

Someone pressed the button and the first notes of Peter's recorded harp music playing 'Going Home' wafted throughout the hospital.

The pastoral services team member said her family

immediately felt an ownership of the new 'Going Home' ritual, since it had begun with them. She was grateful for the compassion that the chief executive showed in honouring her sister's death in this way; it marked her sister as special, as loved, and the family thought of it as something precious that they could hold onto. She invited Peter to play at her sister's funeral where the 'Going Home' musical farewell was mentioned and played.

A three-month trial was conducted into people's reactions and the outcomes were positive. There are not as many deaths as births in the hospital so it is not heard as often as 'Brahms' Lullaby'. Nurses have found the words to explain what the music is about. Some said the music was too short and they would like it longer. This has been done.

And so the hospital now marks birth and death, the full circle of life.

7

ℬ

Contemplating the Dying Time

When I was speaking at the Music Thanatology Association International conference in Oregon in 2006, I met a woman called Polly who, in response to my question about what occupied her days, responded that she was 'preparing for death'. I asked her if she had a terminal illness.

'No,' she replied. 'I'm following a Buddhist path and I want to live my life every day aware of my transience and preparing to die. That means I live my life as well as I can.'

I could sense by her smiling face that this was not a morbid fascination with death. Rather, this was about finding a conscious way to live. She was probably in her sixties, had a ready laugh and sparkling eyes and carried an air of serenity with her. I liked her and I liked her response so much that I too have been trying to become consciously aware of death. I am not Buddhist and I am sure there is deep meaning beyond my understanding in her words, but her words made sense to me.

Recently, I was thinking about impermanence, the transience of life and the certainty of death. I thought about all of the metaphors that are associated with death, the grim reaper, for example. Images of grim reapers and dark angels and thieves in the night are fearsome. If those are the images we have of death, then death is fearsome. After all, death obliterates us. What's not to fear? The survival rate is zero.

Fear of death is what makes us avoid all thought, all mention of it. Some months back an Australian television channel screened the final moments of a man dying from cancer. The channel executives stated that the man had given permission and that their intention was to show that death is not necessarily painful, frightening or humiliating. A national newspaper wrote up the story before it went to air. As I read the write-up, I wondered where we got the idea that death is always painful, frightening or humiliating? The reporter wrote that 'television crosses a line tonight'. In the same newspaper, a number of letters to the editor contained reactions like not being 'able to stomach it', not being 'able to bear watching someone dying, it is far too sad and morbid', and 'this is a freak show'.

Perhaps it is the way death is hidden that leads to our imagining how it must be. And our fear always constructs it in negative ways, as painful and humiliating. While the good death is spoken of as what we would all aim for, the vision that people have of death seems to be of being hospitalised, isolated, marginalised, hidden away.

According to numerous studies reported in newspapers and nonfiction publications about dying, people identify dying in hospital as having others make decisions about them, being drugged, having tubes sticking out of or into every orifice, ventilated, resuscitated, out of control. Sometimes those images are real but sometimes they are not. Death is not always fearful. But when sick and dying people are segregated behind the doors of hospitals, people generally have no awareness of the dying process until they actually encounter it in their lives. They have no awareness of what it is that palliative care offers, or what healthcare workers and volunteers do to bring comfort to the dying time. Death remains unknown and unknowable and frightening.

That same newspaper also printed letters from people praising the television channel for airing this documentary. One commented that it is useful to watch real life happenings that everyone will face one day, saying 'it is demystifying'. Another wrote that 'death is part of life that we like to make unseen and should be made more visible'. Some wrote of good or bad deaths of loved ones that made them see death differently, that an emphasis on respect and dignity replaced fear for them and that it would be 'good for others to recognise this'.

In his foreword to the Zen Buddhist nun Joan Halifax's book *Being with Dying*, the palliative-care physician Ira Byock wrote that we are unique as a species, having awareness of our own mortality and having the capacity to contemplate our own death.

I remember that the first time I was faced with the possibility that I might die was when I developed heart block and required a pacemaker. In the midst of the pandemonium that surrounded me in the emergency department, I was completely calm. There was no fear, more a curiosity: *So this is how it will be?* I handed myself completely to those helping me.

Contemplating the death of another was not quite so calm an experience.

When my husband had a serious accident, falling four metres from a ladder, he was close to dying several times and I remember my distress and the deep anguish of watching and waiting. I put all my faith into the medical staff in the intensive-care ward and willed him to stay alive so he could come home. He did, albeit with serious disabilities, but alive with disability was better than dead and gone forever. He still lives with disability, with declining health. And I still contemplate his death with dismay.

The leukaemia specialist Larry Cripes thinks that most people take their health for granted, and so they plan for the 'what' of their lives rather than the 'if'. This is what my Buddhist friend Polly recognised. We live our lives expectantly, heading optimistically toward our positive futures and of course so we should. We work hard, raise our families and enjoy our friends. We try to stay healthy (well, I do remember failed New Year's Eve resolutions), and we are certainly well versed on those things that are a threat to our health and wellbeing, whether we regard them adequately or not: cigarettes, alcohol, cholesterol, obesity, hazardous driving, and workplace accidents. We have laws and practices and scientists whose lives are devoted to staving off our deaths. All of this is fine, but we relegate death to being somewhere out there, in the future, so we can and do avoid thinking about it. It is not welcome. I do not welcome it for those I love. Analysing my own situation, times where the problem may have created a long terminal illness made me fearful, but when there was an acute condition, I was not. That makes me wonder whether, like those in the studies I have done, it is not death that I fear – the gone-ness of no longer being – but the manner of dying.

So people generally avoid thinking about death. In our fear, we run from it as fast as we can. Then death comes anyway, as it was always going to. We were only ever a heartbeat away from it. Then we describe someone as having been 'taken', as if death is always the unexpected work of some malevolent force. And because we have not accepted it, because we fear it, we are seldom ready. And because we are not ready, we have no words.

We do not know what to say, or how to 'be' with someone who is dying.

Having no words so often leads to a superficial brushing off when a dying person speaks of their imminent death. 'Rubbish, you look great. You'll go on forever,' and then when that person leaves the room, 'Gosh, she looks awful. It must be close.' And the dying person is left with no one to talk to about things that really matter. And the suffering is increased.

Sam De Brito, a columnist with a Melbourne newspaper, wrote about the death of his stepfather. He found it challenging to be in the room with someone who was dying and he struggled with avoidance. It was easier not to go there than to be so uncomfortable in that room where the suffering he witnessed was so distressing.

Reading his column conjured a memory of the first time, as a nurse, I really faced death in a conscious and aware way. The first time I chose to stay and offer whatever I could in comfort. It happened when I was twenty-one and was an encounter with a man I was caring for, who was dying. I was working in an old ramshackle men's medical ward. In those days the beds seemed to be filled with ageless, homeless, alcoholic men who were gruff but had wonderful lived-in faces with twinkling eyes hidden behind bushy eyebrows and yellow teeth (what was left of them) behind great smoke-stained beards. Smoking was not allowed in the wards but there was always tobacco in their beds. And they called the nurses girlie. 'Get us a cuppa, will ya girlie, can't move me bloody leg. Thanks, love.'

I was administering an intravenous medication to a man who lay in the very last bed in the long corridor. His face was skeletal and his skin had a yellowish tinge. His eyes were sunken and dull with deep dark shadows under them. He had metastatic cancer of the throat, against which medicine was still waging a war. He was probably around mid fifties. Not old enough to die. He was weak, tired and in pain. His name was Richard Armstrong.

Richard's eyes hooked mine and he asked quietly, 'Am I dying?'

Shocked, I stopped what I was doing and stared at him. Then I looked around for a rescue. I was taught that as a nurse it was not my place to tell someone they were dying. That was the doctor's job. Nurses did not diagnose in those days and to say someone was dying would be to diagnose. However, in reality we faced those questions from patients constantly. We would be expected to have some glib response to this, certainly not to be truthful. Problem was, though, that often when we nurses knew the end was near and that intervention was futile, the doctors had not given up. We knew people needed time to say goodbye, to put things in order, but in the acute-care environment, time after time we stood by while that time was denied them.

There was no rescue; I was the only staff member there. Even though I felt panic, I had to answer and I could not pretend. I took a deep breath and stepped inside this fragile moment.

'I'm so sorry,' I said. 'Yes, you're getting close to the end now.' I pulled the curtains around his bed. Those little scraps of blue fabric were the only privacy we had. I sat down on the chair beside him and held out my hand.

He took it in both of his. 'Thank you,' he said. There were tears in his eyes.

Richard Armstrong. I remember the name because Dick Armstrong was painted on the side of an automotive business in North Melbourne that I passed every day on my way to and from the hospital. Not the same man, but I saw that name for years and continued to see it years after, till eventually it was painted over. Every time I passed it I thought of *my* Richard Armstrong. Not that I needed any reminder.

We talked quietly for a while. He asked me how long I thought it would take, this dying business. I said I was not sure but probably days rather than weeks. I asked about his family. I knew that he was estranged from his brother, who was his only family. I asked him whether he wanted to sort out whatever that problem was.

He thought about that and then simply said, 'That would be good.'

I left to telephone his brother.

As I walked past the man in the next bed, he said to me, 'That's an amazing thing you just did, girl.' My eyes had welled up so I couldn't really see the accompanying expression.

Years later I still wonder whether he thought I did the right thing in answering Richard's question, or whether maybe he thought that I removed whatever hope Richard might have been clinging to. In my own mind, what I did was the right thing to do and I have never regretted it.

But at the time I said nothing and went on about my mission. I am trying now to remember how I felt at that moment. I think I felt a bit defiant that I had been truthful and forgone the rules I didn't buy. I felt a bit afraid, too, of the possible repercussions. Unsure about whether I had made a mistake in telling the man he'd die soon – it was all a bit over-whelming – I was shaking, but also aware that this moment was about Richard and not about me. That is why I did not respond to the other man: I was focused on my task.

There was shocked silence for a moment at the other end of the phone. From Richard's brother's response it seemed that the shock was as much about hearing anything about Richard after so long as it was about the news of his impending death.

The brother said he would come, and he did, before the end of that day. When he arrived I noticed how alike they looked. He was a bit cool with me but I sensed that it was because he simply didn't know how to act or what to say. I took him to Richard, pulled up a chair and drew the blue curtain for the second time that day.

'Hello, mate,' he said to Richard and put out his hand.

Richard looked at him and smiled with such warmth that the handshake turned into a hug, then into tears.

I was so relieved. I had felt responsible for this reunion and it could have gone wrong. His brother stayed for hours, until Richard lapsed into exhausted sleep. I don't know what they talked about for so long, but what I do know is that they made peace.

After his brother left, I went back.

'What will it be like to die?' Richard asked me.

My reply was that it would probably just be a slowing down and stopping. 'It will mainly be about your breathing, but I will do my best to keep you comfortable.'

We talked a little more about that.

'Will you know when it's really close?' he asked.

I said that I would, and that I would stay with him then. I wouldn't let him die alone.

'Thank you,' he said and closed his eyes.

I went home that night, but when his time was close I didn't. When he died, I cried.

When I look back at Richard Armstrong, I recognise this kind of nursing as the crux of being a 'real' nurse. Once I discovered that I could nurse like this, not shrinking from something really difficult but staying, seeing it through, I wanted to be this kind of a nurse always. I didn't always get it right, but on this occasion I did. I didn't do anything spectacular; I just stayed with him, breaking his aloneness as much as I could.

The person receiving news of an illness that is terminal steps over a border that they hadn't known was there. Richard Armstrong suspected that he had reached that line, but when I confirmed it he knew that there would be no going back. This was uncharted territory for him. No maps exist and no one could tell him how it would really be. There was not much I could offer him but relief of symptoms and my company. Richard with a terminal diagnosis became someone new, he was not who he was the moment before he heard and understood. He would never be that person again.

Roshi Joan Halifax tells us that up to the point of receiving a terminal diagnosis, people live the story they expected to live. Stories I think of are having a career, being a mum or dad, being successful and influential, or being a musician and a healer. Or the story might be believing our kids would not die before us, or that we would die in ripe old age. Whatever the story was that people thought they were living, a terminal diagnosis renders it transient, false even. Now they are propelled into a new story. Now they have to find the means to shape it. What will the new story be? Denying death by searching the world for the cure – the Brazilian jungle juice or the Shamanic faith healer? Or will it be dying well? Dying with dignity? Dying at home, surrounded by loved ones, peaceful and ready, having sorted all affairs and making peace with the world?

If only it was that easy. In reality one has no control at all. We have no idea how this terminal illness will unfold, whether it is even this illness that will be what kills us. We may, for example, die of a heart attack in the midst of cancer, or be hit by a bus.

Whatever we will die from, we do not know how we will experience it, who will help us and in what ways, or what help we will need. We can hope, and prepare as much as possible, letting others know our wishes, but in the end how it is, is how it is.

Until I realised this truth, I had been stuck in definitions of a good or bad death, which had cemented for me in my years as a nurse. There was a day, for example, when, as a student in the men's medical ward, I witnessed an attempted resuscitation. A man with extensive metastatic cancer collapsed and a group of doctors was carrying out cardio pulmonary resuscitation. Suddenly the unit manager, a small, firm but gentle woman called Vera Wade, walked through the curtains and up to the head of the bed. She bent and placed her mouth close to the man's right ear and in a soft but clear voice she said, 'Jesus, Mary and Joseph, I give you my heart and my soul. Jesus, Mary and Joseph, assist me in my last agony. Jesus, Mary and Joseph, may I breathe forth my soul in peace with you.'

And as she said this little prayer for the dying man, all activity stopped. The medical staff stepped back from the bed. The frantic resuscitation activity was replaced by her murmured prayer, the man's last breaths and then silence.

That was a lesson about courage for me. I could not imagine myself doing what she did, but hoped that I would find the strength if I was ever in a similar situation. I also learned that the drama around a cardiac arrest was seductive, saving a life, heroics. But in that moment I understood that some deaths are simply the end of a life cut short by a terminal illness and that sometimes, at the end, it is a death, not a cardiac arrest, and it should be attended by peace and reverence and not by frantic intervention and struggle. Even in acute care, death can be better than that.

Vera Wade. Vera was one of two women who were constant role models for me when I worked with them. The other was Elizabeth Eadie, the unit manager of the neurosurgical unit where I worked for some years. I would give my eyeteeth to be nursed by people like Vera and Elizabeth at the end of my life.

Some years ago I came across an article by Australian author Beverley McNamara that made me catch my breath. She used the words 'good enough death' to describe situations in palliative care where the focus is on relief of physical symptoms like pain and nausea but fails to address emotional, spiritual or what we might call existential issues.

I thought back over my nursing experiences and I knew that I had witnessed, even been part of, someone's death experience that could only be called 'good enough', or not even that. The idea that 'good enough' could be good enough made me shiver. Now I am challenged to give up ideas about good, bad, and good enough.

Roshi Joan Halifax writes from her understanding that death is neither good nor bad; it just is. She thinks that if we could free ourselves of any expectation of how our death will be, free ourselves from the story we might be weaving about our 'good' death, we can just let what happens unfold. Her argument is that we put huge pressure on others and ourselves when we hold onto these images. As a dying person, she does not want to be judged on how well she died. How, she asks, 'can we be at one with a particular moment if we're expecting something? How can we die freely if we're fettered with an expectation of a so-called "good death"?'

As a carer she does not want to live with the sense of failure that comes from feeling that the person she cared for did not die well. Death can be undignified; sometimes there is pain and suffering, there are odours and leakages, wounds that break down, mouth ulcers, bed sores. As a dying person, we cannot control those things. As a carer we can do our utmost to bring about relief and comfort but we will not always succeed.

'How can we really serve others if we're attached to our particular altruistic outcome?' Roshi Joan asks. We expect that our ministrations will make a difference, and when they do not we experience failure. Any attachment we as dying persons or as carers have to good outcomes creates more suffering when that good outcome does not happen.

The task, Roshi Joan believes, of understanding that we have no idea how it will be is to open ourselves to an experience that is far deeper than any story we might construct, expect or wish for; to accept the journey to the unknown, and ultimately, to find the strength to let go.

If we understand that death is death – not good, not bad, just inevitable – then we simply need to *be* with the dying person, doing what we know how to do, doing what feels right, doing our best. We can be fully present, compassionate, bearing witness and offering support in whatever way we know how to. This is about just *being with*, with no expectation of how it should be but rather working with how it is. This has been called 'presencing', and it is the absence of the ability to be present with someone in their suffering that increases suffering.

At the '13th International Caring Conference' in 1991, Rev John Karl gave a paper titled 'Being There: Who Do You Bring to Practice?' His paper was directed to employers and managers, asking them to consider how they support practitioners so that they can do the difficult work of 'being there well' for people.

The title of his paper stayed with me. I was teaching nursing at Deakin University by then but I knew how important genuine presencing had been in my clinical work and I emphasised it in my teaching, suggesting to students that they constantly reflect on who it is they are bringing to their practice each day.

'Developing a conscious awareness of who you are, what baggage you have brought to work with you at the start of a shift,' I would tell them, 'helps you to focus, to lay aside things that would prevent you from noticing, paying attention, stepping into fragile moments when it's needed.'

The person who is willing to be in the presence of another's suffering creates the space for healing. Not healing in the medical sense, but healing in the existential sense, producing peace and readiness. This is what I strove to do, and I hope it was a legacy I handed on. This is what Peter does.

Sam de Brito knew that any time with his stepdad was precious so he had to 'cut the bullshit and get down to things that really matter in conversation'. What he discovered was that words were essentially unimportant. What mattered was just being there, sitting alongside, being a presence.

Describing death as 'the harsh reality of our common fate', Sam thinks that the avoidance common to Westerners is understandable. Death is seen as the enemy. What he came to understand through his own encounters with death is that it is the fundamental boundary that constrains humanity. It is the physical barrier that we are all on one side of, until we move on. It is the emotional barrier that makes us appreciate the life we have, simply because it is, as he writes, brief and sweet; that we will lose it is certain. It is only through acknowledgement of our mortality that we can understand our existence. My friend Polly's philosophy in a nutshell.

8

ß'

Entering the Aloneness

Somewhere I read that there is a tiny fragment of time, maybe just a split second when a baby is born, when it emerges from its mother but before it lands – hopefully in safe hands or on soft cloth – when it is completely silent, completely alone. It has not recognised where it is, doesn't know that there *is* a where to be recognised. It has no idea about people and place, other than the dark warm space it has been in for months. But even then it has no concept of dark because it has never known light. It has no concept of warm because it has never felt cold, so it does not really know that place either. It has no needs because it does not know what need is.

Very soon, it will cry and that will be because it has been stimulated, generally by a doctor or a midwife, and then its eyes open: a breath in and the world starts. There is a future ahead, perhaps, but this child does not have a concept of future, or even of now. In this split second, the child just is.

This is existential aloneness. Writers, philosophers and mystics have always alerted humanity to the fact that we are born alone and we die alone. In between we may experience other states of aloneness but we do not experience that raw existential aloneness that accompanies birth and death.

Loneliness is a kind of aloneness. It is the feeling of sadness in being alone, of longing for companionship. Elderly folk whose partners have died describe the unbearable loneliness they experience, not speaking to a single person for days, never feeling the touch of another. We can be lonely in company too, in a loveless marriage, for example. Or you may be painfully shy, hugging the wall at a social gathering where everyone is laughing and chatting but you do not know anyone. In the end you leave.

In contrast, solitude is a sought-after state where a deliberate choice is made to withdraw from company, seeking to be alone in a quiet peaceful space. I find welcome aloneness in nature; by oceans or fishing in rivers where no fish interrupts my reverie. I find it by the fire in winter, or in a sunny corner with a good book. This kind of aloneness is about contentment in my own company, or about catching up with myself, or healing. It is not usually chosen as a permanent state. Generally we also seek company, since we are social animals too.

Another form of aloneness is the removal of oneself from the world to focus inwardly. This is often described in Eastern religions and philosophies as a meditative or contemplative communion with something greater than ones self, God perhaps. It is also described as getting in touch with your innermost core of being. There are many who use meditation, prayer or some other practice to remain centred, to find balance and harmony in their daily lives. Some – contemplative monks, enclosed religious orders, or mystics, for example – seek this as a permanent state. I welcome these kinds of aloneness, but I am not referring to any of these. Existential aloneness is my focus.

The aloneness of death seems different to that of birth. If we have lived any kind of life at all, we have known time, place and people. Even if times have been hard, places impoverished and people brutal, we have still known. We have lived a life. When we face death we know we will lose that life. And we hold that life is precious. How often do we read about people who struggle to continue to live even when their lives are intolerable? Life is hard to give up.

When a terminal illness is diagnosed, the way we have viewed our life so far is immediately challenged. All the trappings are stripped away, the things we thought were important. Suddenly we are left with the only thing that really matters: our *beingness*.

Ira Byock describes this moment as being called to a place, a desert maybe, where we are left naked, with only our breath, in and out, in this moment of absolutely knowing mortality. This is a time when we are truly alone and we are neither peaceful nor content and in this moment we are not focused inwardly on bliss. From here on we will be aware of life ticking away, moment by moment. We can turn our attention to how we are to live whatever time is left, and on being ready to die, and that may change the nature of the aloneness, but in that first moment of waking up to death, we are alone in a stark way.

I think that Richard Armstrong faced this moment. He suspected, but when I answered his question he was suddenly propelled into a deep existential aloneness. I tried to ease some of it, but I thought I could never enter that space. Now I think differently, and my new understanding has come about by watching Peter and reflecting on what he does and, really, what he is.

I have this idea about what I call the 'existential insider'. I first thought up this phrase in the early nineties, when I reacted negatively to arguments that were rife in the nursing literature at the time that nurses are invisible, and that this is because society values curing over caring, reifies medicine and does not value nurses. What I was reading in the literature was at odds with what I was experiencing in my daily work. I had no sense that those I was caring for did not value what I was doing. The more I thought about it, and watched the people and events in my day, the more convinced I became that what was invisible was the illness experience. Hidden away in hospitals, not for the eyes of the public.

I thought about how I shared this hiddenness. I was on the inside and I knew the secrets. I knew that my insider status was extremely valued by those for whom I cared in my work, because the illness journey is a lonely one that nurses help alleviate. I decided that this explains the apparent taken-for-grantedness of the work of nurses. In a very real sense nurses are given unusual access to the intimate life space, and unless they violate the insideness in some way, they simply merge with it. This is a very different view from that which sees nurses as invisible and powerless because they are asked to care in a society that devalues care.

Once I dreamed up this term, I knew it described what I had previously called the 'real' nurse. It was the nurse in me that I discovered with Richard Armstrong. The existential insider knows about existential aloneness and loneliness, and the difference between them. They recognise both and address them in their care.

Now, watching Peter, I realised that he too is an existential insider, and he too knows about existential aloneness although that is not a term he would use. I am sure there is something in our nature that calls us to the work we do. I know the story of the calling Peter has experienced, which he will describe in the coming chapters. But I know, too, that his training directed him to working in this way. I envy Peter the deep inner-awareness work he was asked to do in his training program, because there was certainly nothing like that in my own. I became the nurse I was because of experience, role modelling by people like Vera Wade and Elizabeth Eadie, and my own maturity as the years went by. I sometimes lament how young I was when I was young, wishing that my patients in those beginning years had the benefit of an older, wiser me.

I watch Peter as he sits at the bedside of someone who is dying. I notice his absolute attention, his mindfulness, his being absolutely in the present moment as he sits with this person. This is the genuine presencing that I have described before. I know that he is accepting of the approaching death and that sometimes, just as Steven Levine describes, he is the only one in the room who is. Sometimes the dying person is struggling to hold on. Other times the dying person is ready to go but relatives are distraught, looking for one more test, one more treatment, and pleading with the dying person to hang on.

In times like that, I have noticed a bond form between Peter and the dying person; he has entered the aloneness. Now there is someone they can talk to about dying who will listen and respond and not push it away. There is such loneliness and suffering when the dying person cannot speak of death to those who refuse to accept it.

Phyllida Anam-Aire wrote a poem in her book *A Celtic Book of Dying*. It describes the longing a dying person has to have someone who can stay, keep vigil without anchoring them to the world:

Can you be with me in the cold morning of dying?
When the fire in me is out and nothing warms my blood.
Can you watch with the eye of a mother?

When the candle is burnt and the friends have gone?
Can you just be, not wishing one more breath in me?

The Irish poet and scholar John O'Donohue calls such a person an 'anam cara', a soul friend. I love that idea. I also came across the term 'an enduring surrounding', coined by Lindholm and Eriksson, who wrote: 'In the "drama of suffering" the patient longs for genuine compassion. The answer to this longing is a sensitive listener who can . . . sustain the mission of compassion in a courageous and powerful way, by being "an enduring surrounding".'

I love this notion of the enduring surrounding too. I think it is another way of expressing my notion of the existential insider. I hope that I was an enduring surrounding or an anam cara for Richard Armstrong, and maybe for many others too. Peter is all of these things.

I have seen friends and relatives of people in palliative care sitting back from the bed, in chairs lined up against the wall. They have no idea how to act, what to say. Peter moves close to the bed, touches the dying person gently to mark his presence and then starts to play. His face is gentle; his eyes do not leave the person's face. He offers himself and his music as a bridge. I have seen people watch him and slowly move to be closer to the bed, touch the person themselves, smile and weep in a different, gentler way. They find a closeness to each other and to the person who is dying. Fear melts away. Peter has shown them by his actions how to be there without fear. He has helped them to step into the aloneness a little further.

People do keep bedside vigils with those they love. They may not know how to act, what to say, but they know that being there is important. Grief is deepened when someone they loved and kept vigil with dies when they are not there.

There were many occasions I observed as a nurse when those closest to the dying person kept tireless vigils for so long and then stepped out briefly, perhaps to attend a mass or for a quick coffee or a phone call, and in that short space of time the person they were with for so long died. They were distraught. This was not about not wanting the person to go – they did not wish them to stay – but just not wanting their loved one to die alone.

Sometimes the person would ask me, 'Do you think it's okay for me to go? Do you think it will be okay?' And sometimes I would say, 'I think so. There's been no change, although it's close.' And so they would go, and I would be wrong.

As my skill as a nurse grew I knew to watch out. When the person left for that short phone call or whatever I would hover, and if I was able to – call bells and urgent need of others allowing – I would wait. I knew that even though it was not much to offer, the knowledge that at least someone was there would help. Somehow a lonely death creates great anguish. I would go into the room because it was unacceptable to me too. I felt devastated if I was called to care for another patient and came back to find that the person had died, alone.

Since those clinical nursing days, I have read about dying people choosing to die when a loved one leaves the room. Even people who seem deeply unconscious die in such moments. The theory is that when the person whose grief is anchoring them to this world is absent, there is freedom to go. That may be so.

Peter has had people die during a vigil, and I have wondered if this freedom to go in those moments was because his work is about helping them to shake off that anchor chain that holds them here. In the absence of someone pleading with the dying person not to go, perhaps the going is easier.

I notice that there is a time in the dying process where people go somewhere very deep. The focus is inward, profound and does not seem to admit suffering. Nurses might say they are semiconscious, but although rousing them is difficult, it is sometimes still possible. If they are roused, they will respond to a degree, but with a deep tiredness and an impatience to return to the state they were in.

I felt when I roused Alice one day that she was in this place. She roused to hear Peter play, but only briefly; she was impatient to go back. When we left she seemed asleep or semiconscious, but there was no sign of distress on her face. This apparent semiconscious state is not a time of nothing happening. It is not sleep. As Phyllida Anam-Aire tells us, there is a profound and meaningful journey taking place and only the person who is dying knows its magnitude. This suggests to me that existential aloneness is not necessarily negative, that it can be a time of locating deep peace and developing readiness.

Once a person no longer rouses at all it is not possible to know any longer what kind of a space they have entered. We can hope that they found a place of peacefulness and serenity and, like Alice and Robert, learnt to take themselves there. That might be the place they leave from. But perhaps it is the need of those who walk alongside that makes them (and us) hope this is so. Perhaps, in reality, it does not matter any more. If they no longer look behind, then whatever is before them we will never know. They are truly alone as they take that next metaphorical step that shuts their mortal body down forever.

The work of the existential insider, then, is to walk to the edge of awareness hoping that whatever support and compassion they offer is enough to ease the deep aloneness, to help a state of readiness so the next step is without fear. Alice and Robert both reached that place for as long as they could tell us about it. We can only hope that it held them when they were truly alone.

I am not a clinical nurse any more, but no doubt I will experience the deaths of others around me, and, sometime or other, my own. I contemplate what I would like for those I love and what I want for myself: an existential insider, a soul friend, someone who is not afraid of death? That is what I want to be, and that is what I want for myself. Someone who can walk alongside as far as it is possible to go, till the person I love, or I, have to move on to the rest of the journey alone.

I have been that. I want to be that. I want to have that.

Section 2

ↇ

Journeys of the Heart

Peter

9

℘

Turning Point

I filled a glass with cool water and carried it across the room to look at the expansive view of the city of Geelong spread out below. I didn't know that I actually needed water; it was just that the sunroom on the third floor was a nice place to take a break. My day had been one with the usual mix of encounters with patients but for the moment I needed a little time out. I was feeling emotionally weary.

The sun on my face and the view of the yachts sailing on Corio Bay was perfect and just what I needed. I had come from the Special Care Nursery for sick and premature babies, where thirty minutes before a tiny baby had undergone a necessary but heart-wrenching procedure. It caused her to scream out in pain in a thin, shuddering voice as the staff tended to her. I played my music to offer comfort to the tiny babe and also to provide a degree of calmness in the room for the young doctor and two nurses who had gathered around the bassinet. It was serious business and they were focused on what they were doing. The best thing I could do was to play. I was told that she would be all right now that it was over, but it was excruciatingly hard to be there and hear that cry. I hoped my music helped her somehow. I knew the nurses appreciated me being there.

I glanced over my printed day list. I had played for patients receiving their infusions of chemotherapy in the day oncology ward. Prior to that I had been in the critical-care unit, and prior to that I had been playing in the surgical ward for a patient dealing with the morning's new reality that his lower right leg had been amputated.

Also, today in the multi-disciplinary care meeting concerns for one or two particular patients were raised. One patient, we were told, was near the end of his life. This prognosis had come unexpectedly and I knew I might be called on at any moment to offer comfort to the family, who would be dealing with loss. The hospital's pastoral-care team members weren't certain how his frail, elderly wife would cope.

The city of Geelong was spread out in a 180-degree vista below me. Separated from the noise and busyness below, visitors to this warm sunroom could gaze across the streets and commercial buildings leading down to the bay. From this distance they could see clusters of tiny yachts and slowly moving container ships on the waters of Corio Bay. This was the place for a pleasant stop and welcome distraction, and I was enjoying mine.

'See that man's harp in the corner, darling? He plays for little girls just like you and I'm sure if we ask him nicely he might play you something. I wonder if he would.'

'Hello, Mr Roberts, you probably won't remember me but I used to come into your shop.' The woman stood in front of me, looking at me. 'My parents bought all their furniture from you when you had Roberts Interiors and I remember it was such a beautiful place. And I've followed your story in the papers and heard about the lovely work you're doing now. My mother will be so pleased to know I've met you here.'

Her face had some familiar features, but I didn't really know her or the little child who were now in the sunroom speaking to me. I broke from my restorative reverie to talk with her.

'So you remember Roberts Interiors?' I said. 'That was a long time ago. Goodness, it almost seems like another lifetime to me now. I think we can even see the old stone building from here if we look hard enough.'

We looked across the buildings of the city together and I pointed out where the furniture shop had been. I asked the woman about her parents and showed the little girl my harp. While I was playing 'Twinkle, Twinkle Little Star' a staff member from pastoral services came into the room and caught my eye. She scribbled something on a Post-it note and stuck it on my harp while I played so as not to disturb the little recital we were having. On the note she had drawn a circle with two eyes and a downturned mouth and the words: *Room 241. As soon as you are free. Many thanks.*

I took my leave from the impromptu nursery rhyme concert for the little girl, placed the harp on its trolley and headed for the family in 241 who were facing sad circumstances.

My days in Roberts Interiors were indeed a lifetime away.

☙

I don't know when the numb feelings began. That's the thing about numbness; it creeps up and overtakes you unexpectedly. By the time you are aware of it, it is too late, it has settled in. Eventually you don't feel anything.

Let me tell you how the numbness crept up and overtook me.

Dealing in furniture and beautiful objets d'art was central to my livelihood. My wife Jeanette and I had taken the lease of a gorgeous two-storey historical sandstone building in the centre of Geelong. We called it Roberts Interiors. The sign attached to the sandstone entrance read: *Fine Furniture. Peter and Jeanette Roberts. Built 1847.*

We catered to the upper end of the market and sold a range of distinctive furniture and interior decor items. This was prior to the birth of our two daughters. We were young, newly married, and full of enthusiasm as we shared the fun of having our own business.

Over the many years we owned it, Roberts Interiors was good to us and we enjoyed a pleasant and reasonably comfortable lifestyle. We made many friends and continued to maintain the reputation established by my parents during the long years they ran their own fine china and glassware business, L'Amour Gifts.

My parents' business was very successful. Both Joy and Harry Roberts were hard workers and good at what they did. As a youth without a clearly decided career path when contemplating leaving school, I felt the unspoken pressure to work for my parents in order to take over their business. Given their established success and my lack of direction, it was a reasonable and sensible option.

After a couple of years' experience working as an executive trainee in an automotive manufacturing business, I did work for my parents. I was at L'Amour Gifts for twelve years, give or take the year or so I worked in the UK in potteries and china stores, and visited china and glassware manufacturers in Europe. I earnestly sought training and experience in the china and glassware industry at the time, but I was also young enough to want to experience life beyond the confines of home and my own hometown.

My father and I were mates, and we worked together well. He was a good boss to his large staff, and both my parents enjoyed friendly relationships with their loyal following of customers. L'Amour Gifts with its china, giftware and homewares was the place for young hopefuls to dream of the lovely things they would need in the establishment of a home in a future marriage.

Those were the days of the 'glory box'. Glory box! What a term! The glory box was a name used to describe a collection of household items put aside for the day a young woman's dream of marriage finally came true. She often purchased a large, carved camphor box to keep her treasures in. At the time of our engagement Jeanette and I worked together at L'Amour Gifts, and because I could see the funny side of it I unashamedly admitted to having my own glory box, even before we met. Mine consisted of a ten-place bone-china dinner setting, plus matching sets of Irish Waterford cut crystal, stemmed drinkware purchased during my working holiday period at the Royal Doulton Potteries at Burslem in England.

In my early twenties I was working at Royal Doulton when they ran their annual Christmas sale of seconds. Seconds were slightly imperfect items of china that hadn't passed the meticulous final inspection demanded before goods were released onto the retail markets around the world. These items were available only to staff members and the piles of beautiful pieces on the trestles were highly prized by the factory workers and office staff who bought them. I couldn't resist a bargain and spent up big.

Having a young Aussie bloke in possession of a glory box laden with fine china was a running joke within our family, and was of course mentioned to embarrass me at my wedding reception in one of the speeches. But I digress.

The decision to break away from my parents' business came to a head once Jeanette and I were engaged and planning our future together. I wanted to do something of my own. Finally, after all those years working with my father, he had come to accept the fact that I would not be taking over the ownership of his business. He would have to make other arrangements if he was to retire. Being the person he was, he offered his support to Jeanette and me, and we moved just across the road from the family store into our sandstone building to make our own mark in the world as a young married couple.

A couple of years later Jeanette and I took on a business partner, Wal Wiggs, an old school friend of mine who was now an accountant. We joined forces, Wal bringing his financial abilities to add to our experience of retailing. We did well and together we grew the business over the next seventeen to eighteen years.

We had one store, then two, then a third, this time in Melbourne. We invested in small commercial properties along the way and began importing containers of furniture to sell in our stores and, eventually, more containers to resell to other stores. Our curtain workroom and upholstery section was doing very nicely too. Elizabeth, our in-house interior decorator, had built up her reputation and ours around the quality of the goods we carried and the services we offered.

They were mostly good times. We enjoyed the stimulation of creating new opportunities for trade and we bounced off each other's enthusiasm for facing a challenge. As the business grew larger and larger, so did the complexities of responsibilities and organisation. The newly married young couple enjoying each other's company as we 'played shop' was becoming a distant memory.

I had arrived at a crossroad. Somehow more than thirty years had passed. All those years involved in retailing. The buying and reselling of beautiful items was my skill in trade, but now my heart was no longer in it. In truth, I didn't know where my heart was. Somewhere during the past three or four years, I had lost the desire to further develop our business. It felt as if it were just growing for growing's sake. A numbing discontent settled within me. I ignored it stoically during those years in an attempt to maintain the status quo and our pleasant lifestyle.

The feeling I was losing was the enjoyment of life. Sadness seeped in, filled me, and weighed on me. I carried a constant heavy melancholy. I was 'just there' for the most part, longing for something more. I didn't know what the something more was; I just longed for it.

I was a husband to Jeanette, a father to our two young daughters. Most people who knew me saw me as a successful businessman and storeowner. I loved my family and the life we shared together, and did my best to support and provide. And yet, somewhere in my mid forties this numbness came over me. Others noticed it; I didn't. I just put it down to life. Life: sometimes good, often average, and for many months at a time, very average. The feeling of going through the motions of living and tending to the mundane became the norm. Eventually most things seemed to be mundane.

To a large degree I became personally lost in my own interior world, a world I felt I couldn't share with anyone. I wouldn't ever have known how to articulate it really; I just knew the lonely feeling of being lost all too well. It was a difficult time.

A deciding moment, a turning point, came for me in the form of a smart, well-dressed young salesman at the annual interior decorating exhibition held in Melbourne at the historic and beautifully restored Exhibition Buildings. Wal and I were there to choose fabrics to cover the new season's lounge suites for our store. The place was alive with spotlights and conversation. Very smoothly dressed and personable salespeople we had come to know over the years were vying for our attention and beckoning us onto their display stands: 'Have a bite to eat' or 'Come and have a drink'. On each trade stand were ranges of gorgeous fabrics, lamps, cushions and artwork, all matter of items beautifully designed, colour coordinated and presented . . . And I could hardly bear to look at them.

At one particular stand pondering yet another range of fabrics, with Wal flipping each colour over one by one in their heavy sample books, I looked up at the striking blue suit worn by the sales assistant. I was distracted by something about his face. What was it? Then it dawned on me. He was wearing contact lenses to match the suit.

It was all too much! I could not bear the superficiality and triviality one more moment. I left the building and walked blindly down the brick alleyways nearby. The corrugated fences obscured me. No one knew me. Hopefully no one saw me as I wept. I was at my wit's end. This moment's grief decided for me the end of my thirty years in business.

10

ॐ

The Call of the Reed Flute

Several weeks later I walked slowly down a trendy inner-city laneway, past tall brick buildings I presumed housed the music store I was looking for. I couldn't find it for the life of me, so I walked back to the main street. The street sign confirmed my choice: Hardware Lane. I was right. I had the correct address, but I just couldn't find a building that looked as though it contained a specialty music store.

I shaded my eyes from the sun with my hand and peered all the way down the long laneway, looking past the assorted cafe umbrellas, diners and coffee sippers seated at the tables that spilled onto the pavement. No signs. Nothing.

Then I spotted it: a discreet sign fixed to the wall higher above me than I expected. Discurio: Classical Music Specialists. It certainly was discreet; I had passed it several times. On closer inspection, the narrow elongated windows actually did have displays of musical scores and posters of recording artists, but I had totally missed them. I took a couple of paces up the grey stone steps, pushed open the wooden door and stepped into an unusually quiet showroom. I had read about this store and thought they might have what I was searching for.

I felt a little uncomfortable. There was a recording of a saxophone and double bass playing lazy jazz in the background, but I had the feeling that everyone in the place knew that another person had just walked into their private domain. There was that same feeling of entering the silence of a library when you knew you had to be on your best, quietest behaviour. I began flipping though racks of World Music CDs. I didn't really know what I was after.

A sales assistant standing behind the counter caught my eye. 'Can I help you find anything in particular, sir?'

I felt a little uncertain, even awkward, as I told him I didn't know exactly what I was looking for, but it was music with an instrument called a ney. I didn't know who played it.

The smart young assistant didn't say a word as he typed something on his keyboard, looking earnestly at the computer screen. 'A ney, you said, sir? Is that correct? You mean the Turkish reed instrument?'

I nodded.

'Yes. I believe we have two recordings by the same artist. Do you have a preference?' He read out both titles.

I didn't know either of them but pretended that the first one he mentioned was the one I was looking for. My heart quickened in anticipation of hearing this exotic music, for the second time.

He handed me the empty CD container with its coloured jacket and indicated that I could hear a sample by using the earphones that were in booth three. I settled myself into the booth, though it was hardly a booth; more a place to stand in semi privacy while you closed the outside world off by placing two huge headphone earpieces over your head to cover both ears. Completely. I glanced down at the back of the CD I held in my hand:

> Traditional Music of Today: Turkey
> *The Turkish Ney*
> Kudsi Erguner

The breathy tones of the low-sounding reed flute entered my headphoned world. I stopped fidgeting and became transfixed by the sound that was entering through the speakers and enveloping me. I closed my eyes to listen.

Slowly the flute began to cry its mournful song, the notes rising then subsiding. Rising again, then bending, twisting, pausing and returning to continue on its way. The sound meandering back and forth but always journeying upward. Always upward. Eventually the flute's song culminated in a shrill heart-wrenching cry.

A wave of emotion swept over me, catching me unaware. I wanted to sob, but held it back. This simple reed flute sang to my depths. I knew then and there what it was to be ravished. Ravished by sound. The need to sob welled up again. How could I allow it in a place like this? My eyes were closed to the world. My head tipped back, listening. Tears were running down my cheeks. What on earth was happening to me?

I wiped the tears from my face with the back of my hand, hoping no one had noticed. I listened to the music again, this time with my eyes open, looking blankly into the store.

The flute's cry rose and subsided, ebbing forward and backward. Slowly, slowly. Languidly returning to its place of rest . . . resting into a new place of silence. I took a deep breath, removed my headphones and placed them back on the hook.

'I'll take this one,' I said to the cashier.

Somehow I had chosen well. The sound on this recording was everything I had yearned for and more. The sound of this strange, exotic instrument, played in this manner, reached deep inside me, way beyond my consciousness, my thoughts, and conversed directly to my heart . . . and broke it. But I wanted more. It had brought such a feeling of longing again this second time. I took my parcel and walked to the car park. I climbed into the hot van and headed for home, thinking back to my first encounter with the sound of this reed flute.

Whenever I was on business in the Fitzroy area of Melbourne, there were two places I loved to visit during a lunch break, and good reasons for visiting both. The huge meals piled on your plate at the Soulfood Cafe ensured a generous wholesome vegetarian feed, but the Spiral Bookstore close by was one of those unconventional, intriguing bookshops that drew you in. Well, me anyway. I usually went there for dessert of a spiritual kind after lunch.

The window displays in Spiral were changed regularly and were always interesting and eyecatching. There were Native American hand drums, shamanic rattles, plaited sweetgrass and beadwork one week; a range of candles, books on self-awareness/self-help and posters advertising guided journeys to healing destinations the next. I loved it. It was a treasure trove for someone like me, who was tentatively exploring beyond the edges of my traditional spiritual beliefs. I came from a relatively conservative Christian background, so this was a safe haven for me to explore in any direction I chose without the feeling of being known. I felt a certain guilty pleasure being there.

Spiral's shelves and aisles were laden with books and artefacts from various cultures: bells, prayer feathers, bundled sage, incense, and brass Buddhas. The board advertising workshops was always a fascination to me.

The Call of the Reed Flute

It was in Spiral that I met Noor, a sales assistant I had come to know during my visits over the past few years. *Noor* or *nur* is an Arabic word that means light, and Noor to me was as wonderful as the bookshop, with her Muslim headcovering and Aussie Blundstone workman's boots peeking out from beneath her long skirt. I enjoyed talking with her. She was a person open to conversations on deeper things.

Noor noticed my attraction to books written by Sufi mystics, in particular to the poems of Jelludin Rumi, the Persian Sufi mystic. Rumi was the founder of the whirling dervishes and I have always felt drawn to them. Many of his poems evoked a longing that seemed to resonate with my own. Noor offered to lend me a tape recording she owned of Rumi's poems being read by translator Coleman Barks.

As I drove back home to Geelong, I slipped the tape into the player and turned the volume up. An African frame drum sounded through the speakers and a strange flute I had never heard before wailed in accompaniment. Then came Rumi's poems, read deliberately and slowly in an accent from the American South. The combination of the poems, the music and those two instruments on the tape was mesmerising. I let the music and words flow over me. Three-quarters of the way through the first side came a particular crying sound of the flute that riveted me, and with it Coleman's reading of this poem called 'The Reed Flute Song':

> Listen to the story told by the reed,
> of being separated.
> Since I was cut from the reedbed,
> I have made this crying sound.

The Harp and the Ferryman

Anyone apart from someone he loves
understands what I say.
Anyone pulled from a source
longs to go back.

At any gathering I am there,
mingling in the laughing and grieving,
a friend to each, but few
will hear the secrets hidden
within the notes. No ears for that.

Body flowing out of spirit,
spirit up from body: no concealing
that mixing. But its not given us
to see the soul. The reed flute
is fire, not wind. Be that empty.

Hear the love fire tangled
in the reed notes, as bewilderment
melts into wine. The reed is a friend
to all who want the fabric torn
and drawn away. The reed is hurt
and salve combining. Intimacy
and longing for intimacy, one
song. A disastrous surrender
and a fine love, together. The one
who secretly hears this is senseless.

A tongue has one customer, the ear.
A sugarcane flute has such effect
because it was able to make sugar
in the reedbed. The sound it makes

is for everyone. Days full of wanting,
let them go by without worrying
that they do. Stay where you are
inside such a pure, hollow note.

Every thirst gets satisfied except
that of these fish, the mystics,
who swim in a vast ocean of grace
still somehow longing for it!

No one lives in that without
being nourished every day.
But if someone doesn't want to hear
the song of the reed flute,
It's best to cut conversation
short, say good-bye, and leave.

Hearing those words and the crying sound of the flute was almost too much to bear. It was as if the flute was singing to me, for me. The words of the poem alluded to that which is experienced as missing in many lives: a yearning for a divine connection. For me, the reed flute carried some primordial connection that reached beyond the content of the words. It knew me. I wanted to know it; I wanted to own one, play one for myself. I played that particular poem over and over, rewinding it and playing it again and again.

Sometime later I came across the following small commentary in a book I owned, *The Essential Rumi*, by Coleman Barks:

Words are not important in themselves, but as resonators for a center. Rumi has a whole theory of language based on the reed flute (ney). Beneath everything we say, and within each note of the reed flute, lies a nostalgia for the reed bed. Language and music are possible only because we're empty, hollow, and separated from the Source. All language is a longing for home . . .

I have always been drawn to a distant call. It keeps resounding in some deep inner way and produces a yearning for something I could never name. I felt that this call was the source of my discontent about my working life, and my search through religion and inner development. 'The Reed Flute Song' poem explained the call and the pull it always exerted. This was the message of the ney to me.

That was my first experience of the power of the ney to stir me in this deeply mysterious way. The need to own a copy of this music myself is what had led me to Discurio. Now, driving home from Discurio through the intense heat of the Melbourne summer, I reached for the air vent on the dashboard of my van. Because there was no air conditioner the best I could do was turn the fan to high and direct all the air vents towards my face and legs. As I bent forward to adjust the vents, I glanced down at the brown paper bag on the front passenger's seat. The words *Discurio: Classical Music Specialists* were printed in black ink.

Along with the new source of fresh air that was now blowing towards me, for a very brief moment I felt a fresh emotional quickening as I thought of my small purchase. My excursion into that music store had nothing to do with my everyday working world. I didn't know it but it seemed I was being drawn towards a way out of my present circumstances. While that CD was just a small personal treat, it turned out that the nature of the music it had within it had far-reaching consequences for me. In a sense, this exotic ney music was reaching me at my depths and echoing back my current predicament. It was opening me. It was the sound of one particular instrument at this specific time in my life that called to me. It seemed to identify an unfocused, deep, mysterious yearning. I could hear it within the cry of that flute.

And so began a search for my own instrument.

A few weeks later I returned to the Spiral Bookshop, to Noor, thinking that perhaps she could help me to find one. She began her search on my behalf. I began my own.

My search took me eventually to a darkly lit Turkish coffee shop in Smith Street, Collingwood where I had previously seen groups of men smoking and playing cards. I thought I would take a chance and ask if anyone here knew of this instrument. Eyes lifted as I entered and asked the waiter if he knew of a flute called a ney. Silence. Some hushed conversation, heads shaking, and card games continuing. A knowing look passed to the waiter from one table.

'You come back next week,' he said.

The next week I was introduced to a man who assured me he could help. I went with him to his high-rise council house and sipped thick black coffee while my host told me about his cousin in Turkey who could procure me a set of neys. For a price. A *big* price, of course. He showed me a video of musicians playing classical Turkish art music. The ney being played didn't do anything for me. It was nothing like Noor's tape.

I was becoming obsessed with a desire to have an instrument of my own. I began searching for a way to contact Coleman Barks in America and by chance found a phone number. I called him. The playing I had heard on the recording *Like This* included musician Steve Coglan, a Mevlevi Sufi. That was the connection, the Sufi link to the instrument. I asked Noor about this and she confided in me that she was a Sufi too and would now make new enquiries for me.

Who were these Sufis, I wondered? I searched and discovered that the foundations of Sufism began as a mystical path within Islam. The Sufi practitioner is one who aspires to live a clean, moderate and balanced life following spiritual laws and guidance in order to bring healing and goodness to all people. There is far more to it than this, of course, but I liked the sound of their aspirations. In the West, Christians and Jews and people from other religious traditions counted Sufis among their ranks. The traveller on the Sufi path increasingly carries the divine qualities of compassion, peace and love for all people. Sufism is most often referred to as the spiritual path of the heart, and a Sufi deeply aspires to achieve intimacy and nearness to their Beloved who is the Creator.

My journey led me to kind Sufis who perceived the significance of my connection to the music, but in attempting to locate and speak to many of these people, the message was usually, 'Don't call me, I'll call you.'

Noor arranged for me to meet Adille, a man who knew how to play the instrument. She had been told he had a large collection of them. I visited Adille's home and met his wife and young daughter, and was excited to see that mounted on the wall was a collection of reed flutes. He spoke to me about the origins and significance of the instrument and was obviously fascinated to have an Australian-born person so attracted to it. He took one down from the wall, kissed it and pressed it to his forehead before handing it to me.

I held the hollow reed flute to my lips as he had shown me and blew across the mouthpiece. After a few breathy false starts I began to make a sound. He was amazed and offered me the instrument to take home. I accepted but felt I couldn't keep it for long, as it seemed so precious.

A few weeks later Adille phoned me to say that he had just met a person who had begun to make neys from special reeds that he found on an island in the Yarra River in Melbourne, of all places. The Yarra River was only an hour or so from my home. I was getting closer. My name was passed on. I was phoned again. I ended up in outer Melbourne having the width of my hand-span measured. An instrument was being custom made for me.

A month or so later I held a beautifully crafted instrument in my hands, admiring its simplicity and the mysterious Arabic inscription etched into the brass collar near its mouthpiece. I realised that I hadn't even considered the price.

'How much can I pay you for this beautiful object?' I asked tentatively.

'I've told my sheik about you and he has instructed me to give it to you as a gift.'

There are no words for the gratitude I felt to these people I did not really know. I still have my ney. I have carried it with me for many years, keeping it close to me. I have taken it with me on travels overseas and it has brought me several adventures, but my playing of it is still very rudimentary. Perhaps there is more to this story yet to unfold, and another part of the journey still to open up ahead of me. Who knows?

Why this reed flute? Why me? I have come to believe that my connection to the sound of that flute and the way it was being played was me hearing my longing for something 'more' expressed by another person who knew and understood what it was. What I was hearing was the mystery of the call of the Beloved at a particular time in my life when I was broken open enough to hear it. Hear it, but not necessarily understand it at that time, nor to know how to answer it.

I had heard that call once or twice in my life before, in different forms, in different ways. I was hearing it again now. This was at a time of real need for me. The call could no longer be denied. The question for me now was: If you hear this call, in what way can you answer it?

I am calling to you from afar,
Calling to you since the beginning of days.
Calling to you across the millennia,
For aeons of time
Calling – calling . . .
Since always . . .
It is a part of your being, my voice,
But it comes to you faintly and you only hear it sometimes.
'I don't know,' you may say.
But somewhere you know.
'I can't hear,' you say, 'what is it and where?'
But somewhere you hear, and deep down you know.
For I am that in you that has been always;
I am that in you which has been always;
I am that in you which will never end
Even if you say,
'Who is calling?'
Even if you think, 'Who is that?'
Where will you run? Just tell me?
Can you run away from yourself?

For I am the Only One for you;
There is no other,
Your Promise, your Reward am I alone –
Your Punishment, your longing
And your goal . . .

11

β'

Testing the Waters

I must have been visibly upset still when I arrived home to Jeanette and the girls after the furniture exhibition and meeting with the man with the turquoise-blue lenses.

Jeanette asked what was wrong.

'It's nothing,' I replied. 'Nothing much.'

But she knows me well. She could tell there was something very wrong. Later that night talking in bed in the darkness she said, 'You know, if you continue to do this I'm scared you'll become very ill. You can't go on. You must find something else to do.'

What else was there? Retailing was all I knew. My business was all I had to keep us clothed and fed, and our girls educated.

Some weeks later, I needed to travel on business to a town called Macedon. The trip was pleasant enough – it is a lovely place – but I didn't really care for my task. I was delivering furniture to one of our customers, who owned a combined furniture store and art gallery, but I wanted to be elsewhere. I didn't know where elsewhere was, just elsewhere, doing something else in some other place.

There was no doubting the quality of the artwork, objets d'art and antique furniture on display in the gallery. The feeling of an endearing oldness and quaintness typical of these places was all too familiar to me. Good taste. Finest quality. That was the message any prospective customer who entered this door would pick up as they gazed around the intriguing, well-displayed objects in the converted historical bank building. It would be a case of the unspoken message of 'You only get the quality you pay for' and all those sales clichés.

The polished floorboards squeaked underneath my foot several paces into the store and a voice called out from a back room, 'Be with you in a moment.'

The gallery manager came to meet me, dusting off his hands with a rag. He had a ruddy, friendly face and spoke with a refined, cultured accent. He introduced himself as Clifford then added, 'But most people who know me call me Cliff.' He reached out his hand to shake mine.

Cliff was dressed in a pair of green baggy corduroy trousers and wore a plaid, open-neck shirt and an unbuttoned, double-breasted blue reefer jacket to top off the outfit. That was the uniform of the day – probably most days – for this art dealer-gallery manager. His clothing and his presence all told me that I was in the company of a cultured gentleman and an astute 'horse trader'. His hair was longish and brushed back, a little unkempt. I noticed that the wings of hair at his temples had gone white and he wore them long and swept back, covering the tops of his ears. I don't know why I noticed that, but it seemed to me that he had lived a different life once. Perhaps he had been an artist of some kind.

We exchanged pleasantries. He mentioned that his love was painting but his livelihood came from his work as a country real estate agent and now he was just looking after this gallery as an interest in his semi-retirement. I didn't believe him. He seemed a little weary and bored with his lot. I felt that he was stuck now with the need to make a living. I imagined that perhaps he hadn't pursued his love for painting as a career and was now too old to change and do anything about it. But he was at least in a gallery.

I unloaded the reproduction antique mahogany bookcase, music stand and distressed-timber pine trunk. He signed the delivery docket, we shook hands and I took my leave, stepping back out into the bright sunlight of the day. I needed my sunglasses. It was glary in comparison to the dimness of the gallery.

I had completed all I had to do. It was mid afternoon but I didn't just want to go home. I wanted to do something interesting . . . something else to finish my day.

It occurred to me that I might be reasonably close to Maldon, a town where an acquaintance of mine lived. His name was Andy Rigby. Andy and I had met infrequently over the years, sharing music at an annual folk music camp held in the Otway region of Victoria. Meeting and getting to know the likes of Andy was one of the side benefits of playing music at these camps. Andy was a harpist, flautist and also had a reputation as a fine Para-Celtic harp maker. Para-Celtic was his term for the Celtic–Paraguayan cross harps he designed and was making. Perhaps I could make a phone call to see if Andy was home.

I found Andy's number in a hotel's well-thumbed phonebook, and dialled it. Andy's familiar, friendly voice answered.

'Aha, Mr Roberts! What brings you to these parts? How is Jeanette? And the girls?'

I asked if he had a moment for me to call in to say hello. He said it would be fine and that he would have the 'billy' on to make tea for me. I think that Andy always had the billy on for everyone. It was his homely, friendly way of offering a welcome.

'It's easy to find,' he said, once he had told me the address. 'You can't miss it. It's a large tin shed with a very small house attached to it.'

I grinned, enjoying his familiar sense of humour and knowing just what he meant. His priorities were to have a workshop first and foremost, and somewhere convenient to live nearby.

I miscalculated and it took ages to arrive in Maldon, but I did find the large shed with a small house attached. I walked down the overgrown pathway and knocked on the door. It opened and kindly, smiling eyes and a broad, beard-covered grin greeted me.

'Come in. Come in.'

Andy took a couple of thick coffee mugs from the wooden dishrack on the sink in his tiny kitchen and proceeded to pour a brew of tea. His kitchen had the appeal of having everything you needed within reach of his small Laminex kitchen table. I wouldn't have to reach far to take down one of his flutes from the shelf above the cast-iron stove. I only had to take two or three steps to reach a harp in the corner or to admire the wonderfully fat acoustic Mexican bass guitar hanging on the wall. Food and musical instruments: they were everything a man could need.

We chatted about things and had a few chuckles reminiscing about the goings on at the music camps over the years.

'I came across something that made me think of you the other day,' Andy said. 'It's an article from the *Folk Harp Journal* I get from the US.' He tried to find it among the papers on the bench but couldn't. 'If I find it again, I'll send it to you. It was something about music and spirituality.'

I was a little taken aback to think that he had put those two things together and that they had brought me to mind. Andy's eyes were friendly, but within them there was a perceptive knowing. Perhaps he knew something about me that I wasn't aware of, or wasn't prepared to own within myself.

Eventually a photocopied article came in one of Andy's recycled envelopes. I opened it to read about a young woman who had left all behind, thrown her belongings in her pickup truck and driven across the USA to enrol in the first school of its kind based at a hospital in Montana. The school was a palliative-care initiative by the hospital for students to learn to play music prescriptively at the bedside in order to assist people who were dying. The instrument used was the harp. The training was for two years at a school poetically named The Chalice of Repose Project.

This glowing report of the success of the music and the personal satisfaction found by Laurie Rasmussen – the woman central to this article – made my heart rise and fall. I couldn't believe it. The notion of someone just giving herself over to something like that seemed so wonderful to me. I couldn't imagine ever doing the same.

My involvement with music has been lifelong. My mother tells of times when she would settle me as a red-faced crying baby by pushing my bassinet closer to the wireless. Not any music would do. 'I had to chose just the right music and then you would settle,' she told me.

My very earliest memory of music is of hearing my parents and their friends gathered around the piano singing, and as a little boy squeezing myself in between the piano and the·wall to feel the vibrations of the piano frame. It was a full-body sound experience. It was thrilling and I didn't think anyone knew I was there.

As a teenager I was a folk singer and with my best friend Svein Koningen formed a folk duo. We played in coffee lounges, jazz clubs and dances around Geelong. A year or so later I formed a four-piece band with friends. We called ourselves The Vacant Lot and I was the lead singer. As I wrote in a song in those days:

> We didn't hit the big time,
> We really didn't get too far,
> But we just had a good time,
> Playing on our guitars.

That about sums up our band's situation: we just had a lot of fun.

As a young adult I was the music man at some of the church groups I attended, playing guitar and leading worship-style singing. Later I went on to lead sound-experience workshops and voice-related workshops within the community too. I gradually became drawn to the healing aspects of music and increasingly fascinated by the way music affected people, including me.

Self-awareness groups were prevalent then and I used every opportunity to explore all that I was attracted to; it seemed a harmless enough interest. I attended a yearlong inner journey workshop run through our mainstream church's amazingly alternative programs. I experienced breath-related rebirthing sessions, sacred dance, poetry, and spirituality study groups. There was much musical exploration within this time too: Mongolian harmonic overtone singing, my fascination with Tibetan singing bowls, the plaintive tones of Native American prayer flutes, running sound-and-silence meditative workshops. It was a long list. I gathered more and more instruments around me into my collection. Along the way I also absorbed an exotic variety of experiential information and sound experiences within my psyche.

By the time I had become a young married man with the responsibilities of a growing business and a young family, I had put this interest largely to one side; but it was still there, apparently dormant, waiting for me. At the crossroads of losing a sense of direction in my life, coupled with the feeling of losing my interest in a long-held, safe form of livelihood, I was given an article about The Chalice.

The possibility of doing something like this, given my hobby with sound and musical instruments, wasn't such a strange idea on one hand, but to consider actually *doing* it was something I couldn't comprehend. How could I justify it to myself, to my family, to anyone? It seemed so obscure. I put the article in the drawer of my bedside table, to find and peek at every once in a while. And so the tug of war began.

I had commenced counselling with a spiritual director, a kindly, wise man who perceived my very strong fascination with the American training.

'Why not just send for a brochure?' he suggested.

What harm could be done by that? I thought to myself.

I received the brochure soon enough, and I was a goner. They described the three levels of certification and the aim of creating 'sacred space' for a patient through the use of music, and of 'anointing' people with sound. The poetic descriptions of what they were offering through music were enticingly seductive to a bloke like me.

My goodness, what a tug of war! My logical reasoning knew the implications of doing this would be catastrophic. Leave the country? Two years? How would I make a living? What about my family? Jeanette? The girls' schooling? My business? To do what exactly?

Impossible!

I applied.

Sometime later I received a letter to advise that I had been accepted for an interview . . . in the United States! This was now becoming serious. I reasoned to myself that I had to at least go for a look.

In Easter 1994 I flew to Missoula, Montana via Vancouver, BC and Spokane, Washington. Arriving in Missoula on the Saturday and walking through the timber-beamed airport in Missoula was exhilarating. For one thing there was a seven-foot-tall stuffed grizzly bear rearing on its hind legs to greet travellers. Now that was different! There were glass showcases of matching pine-log bedroom furniture, and elk screenprinted T-shirts, displays of huckleberry-filled chocolates, fishing lures and rods and hats with feathered hooks attached to their brims. Some of the locals waiting to meet travellers wore tight blue jeans, fancily stitched high-heeled cowboy boots and large rimmed hats. By all the signs so far I felt I was now certainly at my destination.

I collected my bags from the carousel and waited. Before I left Australia, a fax had arrived to inform me that I would be collected by someone called Cherri and billeted at the home of one of the Sisters of Providence who ran St Patrick Hospital where training took place. Her name was Sister Elsie.

When I found Cherri, she said, 'I'm afraid Sister Elsie's out of town for Easter but she's left spare keys in the mailbox. She told me to tell you to make yourself at home, and that your bedroom will be downstairs in the cellar.'

We drove from the airport passing by the hospital and turned into the street where Sister Elsie lived. It was a plain, tall, double-storey, grey-painted weatherboard house with white trim. We checked the mailbox. No keys! Cherri had slipped out from work to meet me and needed to return soon. I told her not to worry, that I could easily wait around until after her shift when we could sort something out. And so we hid my bags behind some bushes by the front door and Cherri drove off leaving me to sit on the steps of this empty house in an unknown town I had come so far to visit.

As it grew dark it became bitterly cold. I wasn't used to this. The remnants of slushy wet snow lay on the road and the biting April wind from the mountains cut through the inappropriate clothing I was wearing. I decided to take a walk along the street instead of sitting and freezing on the steps.

I tramped along the footpath. Trees lined each side of the road, leafless, their bare branches reaching across the sky forming an eerie canopy. I became colder and felt more disappointed with each step. I found a diner, entered and ordered a burger and accepted the obligatory free cup of coffee. The warmth of the building and the plate of food helped a little.

Cherri returned with the key. She apologised and said she had to leave again, but informed me the school would start right after the Easter break and I was welcome to come across to the hospital to meet everyone. The school was housed on the fourth floor of the old part of the hospital building. She told me I needed to be there at eight am sharp, in two days' time. I fitted the key into the lock and let myself in.

Here I was, alone in a stranger's empty house. I found a stairway leading down to my bedroom in the basement. Downstairs there were a couple of bedrooms and a bathroom. It felt a little scary being alone downstairs in this unfamiliar house. I went back upstairs, turning on as many lights as I could along the way. I settled into an armchair and surfed through sixty-odd channels of pulp entertainment and advertisements until I could stay awake no longer, eventually going to bed and falling into an exhausted sleep in my dark underground vault.

℘

The morning brought a new day. I awoke, showered and dressed, and found some cereal in a cupboard upstairs in the kitchen. There was also a supply of milk and orange juice in the fridge. This was better. I was ready for an adventure.

I stepped out onto the footpath and walked across the road to the hospital. It was a relatively large building and I circumnavigated the grounds to get my bearings. I decided I needed a car rather than walking, so I hired one and drove off for my first time in a left-hand-drive vehicle on the 'wrong' side of the road.

Having a car was a godsend. I was able to explore Missoula from one end to the other at my leisure. The city was nestled in a valley at the foot of the Rocky Mountains and there were pleasant and not so pleasant suburbs, as is the case in any city, but the area around the university with its wide, tree-lined streets appealed to me greatly. So did the hilly regions, the streams and flowing rivers surrounding the town. I was growing to like the feel of this place.

Having explored most of the township, I eventually turned my car up onto the freeway that led to the Indian reservation at the foot of the Mission Mountains. With my car heater on and country music playing on the radio, the excitement of just being here to explore this place was sinking in. I felt a growing wave of contentment. I was enjoying the freedom of being on my own. Free to choose whichever direction I wanted to take.

The Easter long weekend passed and at eight am sharp on Tuesday morning I arrived at the hospital. The front entry to the old St Patrick Hospital building had a large rubber floormat. When I stood on the mat, two large sliding doors opened to let me into a closed-off area that required stepping forward again for a second set of doors to open. This was obviously some form of weather lock to keep the cold weather from blowing into the building. I stepped forward and the doors opened to let me in. I made my way up to the fourth floor Chalice office and looked around for someone to introduce myself to.

'Oh, you must be the Aussie guy,' a friendly, accented female voice called out to me. It was Deanna, the office person I had been writing to with all my questions during my application. 'Welcome, Peter, it's so nice to finally meet you. Everyone! It's Peter the Aussie guy. Come and say hello to him.'

There was much fussing about and many warm welcomes by the office staff and the few students standing around.

'Now,' said Deanna, 'we have an itinerary organised for you and I'll bring it to you later, but today we've arranged for you to attend on the first class of the day. Before every class there is schola cantorum, or choir. You're just in time.'

I was ushered into a classroom where I spotted half a dozen harps standing ownerless at the very back of the room. Desks had been pushed aside and a largish group of people had assembled, facing a woman who was about to conduct them in song.

'Peter!'

She knew my name.

'Come join us. Stand in the back row next to the other guys. Just follow the music as best you can. It's lovely to have you with us.' This was Sharon, a Chalice faculty member.

I shuffled my way in amongst the group, where everyone was holding sheets of music. They were focused and intent on the directions to start.

The conductress counted us in: *one and two and three.*

The voices lifted in song and I was enveloped in the most beautiful sound I had never heard. I listened as they sang an ancient Latin chant, eventually closing my eyes to my tears. This music was the reason I was here.

I was home.

And so it went on. Throughout that day there were harp solos, thought-provoking lectures, more harp solos, more lectures, a coffee break and a chance to meet the Chalice students, then lunch at the hospital cafeteria. I was introduced to three other new arrivals like myself, visitors to Missoula who had come for their interviews too. One woman was a harpist from an orchestra in Spain, another a former music teacher whose husband had recently died of cancer, another a free-spirited music therapist from the east coast of the United States . . . and me, the furniture retailer from Geelong who could barely read a note of music and couldn't play the harp at all.

'Tomorrow you'll meet Therese,' said Deanna as she handed me the itinerary. Therese was the academic dean of the school. 'But tonight we're going for drinks at the watering hole after class. You're welcome to join us if you like.'

The watering hole was a hotel called The Depot. It had a lounge large enough to accommodate twenty-something noisy chatting people. I liked this group and the easy way they related. I was feeling more and more at home.

I returned to my accommodation that evening and met Sister Elsie, my host. We had a meal together and a couple of beers drunk straight from the bottle. This was an interesting nun. We hit it off immediately. She had a down-to-earth way about her and from what I could perceive stood no nonsense. She was deeply spiritual in an open, uncomplicated way and was known for her work in leading women on self-awareness retreats.

'They all call me the New Age nun,' she chuckled.

When our conversation turned to The Chalice she alluded to the fact that there was more to the place than appeared on the surface. She wouldn't say more. I was intrigued by her statement and felt a little wary of what she was saying.

I retired early as I had my interview ahead of me the next day. I had brought with me my best jacket and the tie, trousers and shirt I always wore to business functions, ready for this interview. I ironed my clothes before I went to bed so that I would be set for the big day.

The following morning I went to The Chalice office to meet the academic dean, Therese Schroeder-Sheker. I felt that I looked quite sharp. I was led into an office used as an interview room.

'Oh my, he's all dressed up and he's even wearing a tie,' one woman said.

They all laughed. I felt humiliated and embarrassed and could feel my face flush. 'So, Peter. Let's find out all about you,' Therese said.

I really don't know what I said after that. I wasn't thinking too clearly. The questions were about my reason for applying for their training, my musical background, my personal interests, and so on and so on. I felt I managed to make sense and hold my composure despite my discomfort at the laughter.

'Well, Peter,' said Therese, 'thank you for your time and for coming all this way to see us. You know, there've been one hundred and twenty applicants from all over the world and we can only take twenty at the most, so we must consider each applicant carefully in fairness to the others.' She paused. 'Now, before we let you go we'd like you to sing for us.' An expectant pause followed this statement.

'What do you have for us to hear?' Therese said.

I was completely unprepared for this. My mind went totally blank. I couldn't think of one song. Then a thought did come to me. It was the only one I had. I had no option, but I was reluctant to offer this idea into the silence that hung heavily in the room.

'The only thing I can think of is Mongolian overtone singing,' I said. 'This is really a form of prayer for me.'

I asked them if they wouldn't mind adopting an attitude of prayer, so they closed their eyes. I sang from my heart the split-toned Mongolian singing I had the knack of doing. The song went on for a time, the notes ringing higher and higher as I improvised with the harmonic overtones inherent in the style of chant. I tapered off the sound to bring the song to its conclusion and we all sat with our eyes closed for a moment.

I felt a stunned silence in the room as my interviewers refocused themselves, opened their eyes and looked towards me again. This style of singing wasn't what they were expecting at all. I had no choice in the matter but wondered if I had made a huge error in offering this obscure chant. Not much else was said between us.

There was a soft 'thank you' then more silence as I left the room.

I walked down the hallway, preoccupied with my discomfort as a result of the interview experience, past the open door to Sister Elsie's office. She spotted me and beckoned with her finger. Sensing something was wrong, she invited me in and closed the door behind me. I told her about the laughter and my initial feeling of embarrassment during the interview process.

She thought for a while. 'It's a good thing that you've experienced this now, at this early stage. I mentioned last night there were things going on below the surface of The Chalice and you've just experienced something of it. While this programme is all about light and goodness, and it is, there's also a shadow side here.'

She went on. 'I have my office just outside the classrooms of The Chalice for a reason. I have appointed myself spiritual guardian of you all. Feel free to come here whenever you want. I'm here for you.'

Sister Elsie then offered a blessing and a prayer of protection for me and for safety on my homeward journey.

'You will be back, you know,' she said, smiling. 'You have something of importance to teach the others. You bring your own gift. This work is much larger than what's here at present. It's about training people in the essence of the work, but the work can't be contained just in this form. You remember when you came into this building? The doormat that opened the two doors? The lesson in that is that you have to walk towards the doors for them to open. You, Peter, have walked towards this path, this work. I believe the doors will continue to open for you, my dear friend.'

A few days passed and I eventually boarded the plane to return to life in Australia. Three months later I received a letter to say I had been accepted into training.

12

ℬ

Leaving the Shore

Between the conception of my dream and the reality of achieving it lay an untrodden path. I found myself tried and tested at every turn as I pursued the hope of moving to America to study at The Chalice. Jeanette and the girls underwent their own trials as their husband and father attempted to turn himself, and by default them, towards the distant vision he had seen, away from the security of all that was familiar to us as a family.

I lost sight of the vision many times over the next months, but remembering what I had experienced in Missoula helped keep my focus clear and my determination strong.

Major challenges were yet to come but the immediate issues at home were difficult enough. A major one was broaching the heart-to-heart discussion Jeanette and I needed to have. I knew I could offer no security in the path I was considering. My vague hope was that in following this musical path I might regain a lost sense of personal identity. From any rational point of view my proposal seemed a vague, narcissistic ideal.

What a darling woman to even hear me out. What a wonderfully brave one who in the end supported me fully in my attempt to realise it. Jeanette would have to leave the beautiful new home we had built together by the Barwon River on its five acres of land in Geelong. She would also need to come to terms with the thought of leaving her family and friends and the work she was enjoying at the Wintergarden Antique Gallery.

What of our financial future and our security? What of our home? What about the girls and their education?

This was a time of anxiety with many days of heavy-heartedness for us both. But with those feelings also came faint glimmers of having new adventures together, midway through our lives.

Both our daughters were attending a private school in Geelong that offered many opportunities for personal growth and encouraged academic excellence. Ellise was young enough to just be there enjoying her friends. She liked sport, her art projects and music, and of course Socks, her pet rabbit that was housed in a hutch among the vegetable plots in the school's Environmental Centre. Katherine's studies were now becoming more seriously focused towards future career choices. She was halfway through year eleven, doing very well academically and was being fast-tracked for year twelve and university entrance. I fretted over the outcome of the changes to these two young lives.

One day during a walk along the river near our home, I had a serious father-daughter discussion with Ellise and broached the subject that she might possibly have to leave her school and her friends to go to America to live for a couple of years. Hand in hand we walked as she quietly and seriously considered this possibility, weighing up the situation in her young mind.

She eventually looked up at me and asked seriously, 'If we go to America, could we visit Disneyland?'

My darling daughter and I struck a deal then and there. Disneyland it was. Ellise was satisfied. She would be the envy of all her friends.

Katherine's decisions were more complex. Some teachers were concerned about interrupting her academic future, and they passed their concerns on to her, unknown to us. The career adviser told her privately she shouldn't go at all but should stay on as a boarder at the school until she had completed her studies. I can only imagine the pressure she felt carrying the burden of that decision.

An interview with the school headmaster ensued, with her father attempting to sound confident as he explained the reasons for leaving Geelong and taking the girls out of school. My explanations weren't understood nor appreciated and showed in his cool gaze.

'Music-thanatology? I don't know that I've heard of it before,' he said. 'I didn't realise you played the harp either, Mr Roberts.'

I sensed a touch of amusement in his tone. How I wish I could have assured him that I did. I was skating on the thin ice of uncertainty in front of one who dealt in logic and absolute certainties. My mention of playing harp to people who were dying, singing ancient chant and attendance at a school curiously named The Chalice of Repose Project didn't help to assure him either.

Many weeks were spent seeking options for helping Katherine through her dilemma. There was the boarding-school option, or completing her VCE studies by correspondence. We travelled to Melbourne to find out if the internationally accepted Baccalaureate certification was a possibility for her.

In the end Katherine only wanted to be with her family. She packed her books and precious notes, taking them on the plane with her, hoping for the best. She left her VCE studies in

Australia at year eleven, leaving The Geelong College to attend a school eventually allocated to us in the States and paradoxically named Hellgate High. The irony of the name was not lost on me. How could I do this to my gorgeous teenage daughter?

And so the complex decisions and arrangements continued, week after week, as we made plans to leave home.

There were some lighter moments. When the girls' school friends asked why they were leaving Australia, they took to saying that their father was going to school in America to train as 'a harp specialist', but by mumbling the word harp it sounded like 'heart specialist'. I can only presume parents at home shook their heads in wonder to hear that the city furniture retailer was making this amazing change to a medical career as a heart surgeon.

I advised my staff of my impending departure and negotiated a financial arrangement with my business partner, who now had to shoulder the responsibilities of our firm independent of me. I had to find a tenant for our home and a purchaser for my car in order to help pay the four airfares to the States.

We each had to choose and pack the restricted number of personal possessions we felt we needed. We boxed and stored the remainder in the barn on our property. Nothing fell neatly into place. This was a trial that tested our ability to persevere right to the end.

One serious issue persisted: the arrangement of a student visa by my school. Many faxes and phone calls were exchanged. The Chalice encouraged me to keep moving towards my goal as apparently 'all was in hand' at their end. Each time I contacted the administrators they assured me plans were 'nearly there'. I didn't need this additional anxiety.

I had travelled to the US Embassy in Melbourne a few months prior, to assist the school in understanding what I needed from them in order to get a visa. The Chalice administrators were making their own enquiries in the States on my behalf. It became apparent that this application process was new to them.

Therese sent a message telling me: *Keep packing your bags. We will see you in September.*

I couldn't mark time. There was a multiplicity of practical details to take care of in order to leave in time. I could only rely on assurances from The Chalice people and trust that somehow fate would intervene on our behalf.

Eight weeks before we were due to leave Geelong, I still hadn't found an appropriate tenant for our house. I needed one because I had secured a lovely home in Missoula for us to live in and I had committed to it by paying a month's rent in advance as security. Our few boxes of personal possessions had also now been sent in advance for collection at the Spokane airport a few weeks later. We were absolutely committed and there was no turning back.

Six weeks before we were due to leave I hadn't found a buyer for my car either. I needed that money.

Then things happened quickly. An executive from the Shell Oil Company arrived from overseas to work in Geelong. He leased our home at a premium rental that almost covered the cost of the home we were paying rent for in the States.

John Hall, a business associate, mentioned in passing during a conversation that he needed a car for his wife. I told him about my Volvo wagon and he offered to buy it unseen on trust, not questioning the price.

'Are you sure you don't even want to look at it?' I asked.

'It's Peter Roberts' car, isn't it? I trust you. I know it will be just fine.'

Our English tenant and his family moved into our home. Jeanette, the girls and I moved to cramped quarters in a nearby motel. The girls were still attending school as Jeanette and I attempted to keep their lives as normal as possible.

I spent my time feverishly dealing with paperwork: legal documents, visas, travel insurance, bank statements, and gathering any official paperwork I thought might be pertinent for our time away. Thank goodness I did.

Our time was now down to weeks, then days. The day before we were due to leave, the school still hadn't sent me the long-awaited student visa form. It was an understatement to say that I was in desperate need of it now – our flight was to leave the very next morning. This student visa, we were told, would enable both of us to work part time in the States. I felt I would be able to find part-time work to support us. I didn't care what. Jeanette was a registered nurse and we had been assured that she would find work within St Patrick Hospital where the school was housed.

I was in a desperate situation that was way beyond my control through no fault of my own. What could I now do but trust in the outcome?

I had the fallback scenario in the back of my mind. I had planned our flight to the USA via Vancouver, so if we had to we could wait there for the visa. Should the worst come to the worst, we would cut our losses, visit Missoula as tourists, have a nice holiday and return home.

I sent another urgent fax that night: *This has gone way beyond a place of despair now, to a place of resignation. There is no way now but forward. If you hear any news I will be staying at Outrigger Prince Kuhio hotel in Hawaii.*

ß'

We left Tullamarine airport in Australia having burnt all our bridges. We were financially and emotionally committed, but without the all-important student visa. This was ridiculous!

The next day in Hawaii a fax arrived at the office of the Outrigger Prince Kuhio Hotel in Honolulu:

Dear Peter, Good news!! We have just received word from the INS that the school has been approved. I will receive the official papers early next week. I will then send you the 1-20 MN form so that you can get your student visa. Do not enter the country without your visa stating you are a prospective student otherwise you could have problems getting the status of your visa changed. I hope this information eases your concerns.

The easing of concerns was an understatement. Fate was with us after all. Now that my visa situation seemed to have been resolved, we could enjoy Hawaii. It was time for a much-needed holiday. Hawaiian beaches, sunshine and the lack of having to deal with constantly pressing issues have a way of helping stress fall away. We became carefree tourists in that gorgeous tropical destination and had a wonderful time together.

The city of Vancouver was fascinating too. There was so much to see and it was all new and exciting. A week later, the details of the visa application took me from joy to despair. I took the school's letters confirming my status and waited in the aliens' line at the US consulate.

No number of lengthy explanations from me, nor details on the forms provided by the school, would suffice. The woman speaking to me through the small round hole in the security window quizzed me fiercely. I felt my blood pressure rising.

She wanted a marriage certificate, birth certificates and detailed proof of past employment.

'I can't understand the connection between what you were doing in Australia and this music training you're going for,' she said. 'The two aren't related at all. Can you explain to me exactly why you're doing this?'

My blood pressure rose further. I was becoming exasperated with frustration and eventually I blurted out, 'Because I am called to it.' I had never used those words to anyone before. I felt foolish as soon as I said it.

'Oh, I see, and who called you?' she threw back at me.

I felt the touch of a young hand on my shoulder and a whisper, 'It's okay, Dad. It's okay.'

I think it was Ellise. This compassionate, soothing touch from my child in my time of despair was almost more than I could take. God bless her. I could have burst into tears on the spot, such was my frustration, but I held it together for further terse questioning.

In the end, this US gatekeeper actually seemed mostly preoccupied with the amount of money we had to support ourselves. I produced the bank statements I had brought with me. They looked healthy enough because of the sale of my car. The money in fact had been mostly spent on airfares, but that didn't show.

Eventually she looked at the bank statements, the date, the amount they showed and then looked me straight in the eye. She loudly stamped my passport without looking down. *Thud!*

'Next please.'

I looked down at my passport as we walked away from the window. She had only given me a visitor's visa. There was nothing I could do about it. I was devastated. This meant we couldn't work to support ourselves.

Later that night I consoled myself with the thought that at least we could get into the States and try to sort something out once we were there.

We flew to Spokane and collected our boxes from customs. Our few belongings and suitcases looked lonely in the back of the oversized U-Haul truck. I closed the back door and secured it. We climbed into the cabin and slowly drove off. We were on our way.

Driving across the mountains to Missoula with Jeanette and the girls crammed together in the front cabin was just wonderful. We laughed at each other's attempts to imitate the American accents we encountered. We stopped along the way at lakes and ate at roadside diners. The scenery was breathtaking. The trip was exhilarating.

The last few miles into Missoula revealed the mountainous valley it was nestled in. We arrived just on dusk as the lights were appearing in the city below us. Missoula looked gorgeous.

Jeanette and the girls had seen the videos I had taken of our new home during my previous visit and now I could show it to them firsthand. I drove carefully into the familiar street and there it was, the large white house on the corner. They all loved it. I was excited to show them and it was comforting for me to know we would be living together somewhere safe and pleasant. This historical two-storey home set within the lovely, leafy neighbourhood of the university district was now ours to live in.

By the time we unloaded our boxes and looked around, it had become dark and the lovely, large but unfamiliar house felt a little scary. We dragged our mattresses into the empty lounge room and slept together that first night. We were in Missoula.

Then came the exploring and the unpacking and the buying of food and household items. The girls decorated their rooms with the belongings they had brought with them from home. We were settling in nicely.

The city of Missoula has a wide, fast-flowing river running through its centre, dividing it in two. We had to cross the bridge over the water each day as we walked into town. The natural setting of the town was stunning and uplifting. We felt healthier just by being there and breathing in the clear mountain air. We had time to explore the city and find schools and books for the girls. Hellgate High was just across the road from where we lived. It seemed a good school despite the name, but Katherine eventually went to Sentinel. Ellise settled into her school quickly.

Their father made his plans to return to school again after thirty-one years.

13

The Chalice

The creation of my school was a palliative-care initiative of St Patrick Hospital and they had invited Therese Schroeder-Sheker, the founder of the program, to relocate from her position at Regis College in Denver where she had developed her music-thanatology program. They were keen for her to train students within the hospital.

Therese was a softly spoken and charismatic woman. She was a gifted harpist with a shimmering soprano voice and was deeply versed in medieval literature.

The two-year training focused entirely on end-of-life care. The primary purpose was to train musicians in the use of prescriptively played music (harp and voice) to be offered at the bedside of dying patients to assist them in their leave-taking. The offering of live music in this way provided emotional and physical comfort to the person when no more could be done medically. The spiritual nature of the musical encounter was intentional and evident to all, the offering beyond specific religious affiliations.

The school and its unique services were becoming highly regarded within hospitals, hospices and medical facilities and now there was an increasing need for more practitioners, more musician-clinicians.

Each training programme ran in two-year cycles, taking around twenty students each cycle. The curriculum was deep and specific to the work of caring for the dying. It promised the exploration of personal inner development and spiritual dimensions that were necessary to bring to the bedside work. This was what I had come so far to discover.

On my first day of school I walked the mile or so across town and crossed the bridge over the swiftly flowing Clark Fork River as I went. I arrived at St Patrick Hospital to step on the same pressure mat I had encountered several months earlier on my first visit here. The automatic doors opened wide for me once again.

The highly polished floor tiles caused my rubber-soled shoes to squeak when I walked. I was aware of the sound of every step as I crossed the hushed foyer to the stairwell housed to the right of the elevator. Instead of taking the elevator I strode to the back stairs, climbing them two at a time, and arrived near the area where I had attended my interview.

People were gathering around the classroom door and others were inside, standing in small groups. All but three were strangers to me. My eyes met those of the three women I had met before and we smiled in welcome recognition. They were the ones who attended their interviews the same week I had. We had made it! It was so nice to see them again.

How could we have known at that moment just how close this entire group would become through the many challenges we faced together over the next couple of years? Therese Schroeder-Sheker, with her penchant for Latin names, eventually nominated us as her 'caritas class', the name meaning 'love for all', such was our support and affection for each other.

We were officially welcomed by members of faculty and asked to form a large seated circle. We were invited to share stories of our journey towards this first day and the reasons we had for being trained to play music at the bedside of those who were dying. Tears flowed as people told personal stories of the loss of loved ones or the hardships encountered in embracing their change of direction.

One woman who had cared for her dying husband told us that she spent forty years working alongside him in their hardware business and how she hated every moment of the forty years in that store. She saw this training programme as her chance at last to do something for herself. A way to feed her soul through playing more of the harp music she loved so much.

Another woman, recently separated, brought her two young boys and all her belongings in a large rental truck that she had driven herself, travelling across the country in order to start a new life doing something she felt drawn to. Leaving an office job, she now had to find a way to financially support herself and her young family during the next two years of training.

Others had left careers and were making a complete change in direction too. Most would be scraping by financially. The sacrifices people were making in order to embrace change were deeply moving.

We had amongst us music teachers, a concert harpist from Spain, a music therapist, several nurses, a jeweller, a radiological technician, a carpenter, and of course a furniture retailer from Geelong. There were about twenty-six of us chosen for this intake, our ages ranging from nineteen to sixty four. We had come from all walks of life but all had in common a deep sense of calling to this destination.

We weren't to know it in the early days, but we quickly came to realise that this course had the intensity of graduate-level education. The individual commitment that was required to stay on top of the amount of work was extraordinary. Not all were able to manage the workload or the pressure and at the end of two years there were only seventeen of us remaining.

I personally hadn't been to school full time for over thirty years, and while it was never presented to me as a prerequisite for doing the course, I brought with me the additional burden of not being able to type or read music.

The range of subjects was embedded in what Therese called an 'infused curriculum', where everything taught was intended to broaden and deepen us on many levels solely in preparation for playing at the bedside for those who were dying. The training was stimulating but very challenging.

A large faculty of distinguished guest lecturers flew to Missoula periodically from across the United States. Rabbi Jonathan Oberman, an authority on Kabbalistic mysticism, spent several days with us. We had Father Michael Driscoll, a priest who had recently arrived back in Montana after working several years in the Vatican. Professor Fred Paxton, a medieval historian from Connecticut College, visited us often. Anthropologist Professor Alice Reich was from Regis College in Denver. Dr Robert Sardello, author and co-founder of the School of Spiritual Psychology in Texas, was a regular. Pat Hopkins, an engaging and warm person, was co-author of *The Feminine Face of God: The Unfolding of the Sacred in Women*. Pat's presentations were popular. One of her themes, 'Spirituality and Pioneering', forewarned of the challenges we were to encounter in the years that followed.

There were classes on anatomy and physiology, end-of-life disease processes, medical terminology and pharmacology, the history of music in medicine, and the evolution of the hospice movement.

We had Buddhist practitioners, doctors, nurses, and hospice directors come to speak to us. We were taught various cross-cultural attitudes and spiritual beliefs relating to death and dying and the way rituals were integral to meaningful ceremonies.

Despite the Chalice program being run in a Catholic hospital, we were not required to conform to a particular religious bias, but were instead encouraged to nurture our own individual spiritual practices whatever they were, in order to underpin the work we were being trained for.

Apart from the lectures, we attended private weekly harp and voice lessons, harp ensemble practice, and schola cantorum. Our training in music theory, musical analysis and the reflective, contemplative approach to musicianship was central to the discipline of music-thanatology. There was also a large repertoire of music to memorise that would eventually be used in end-of-life musical vigils.

We played in community showcase concerts throughout the year and it certainly required full-time commitment from us all to do these in conjunction with the innumerable synopses of lectures, readings and project assignments.

I faced enormous challenges quite apart from my lack of typing and music-reading ability. My very first synopsis submission of the required reading, *Acoustic Symbolism in Foreign Cultures* by the German Musicologist Marius Schneider, had a cover sheet with the title, date and my name, but inside were two blank pieces of paper with a written apology. At that stage the subject matter was far beyond me.

But I persevered. Slowly and painstakingly, tapping one finger on the letters of the keyboard after another, I learned to type. One faulty, awkward pluck of the strings after another, I learned to play the harp. My musical memory and ability to play by ear confounded and frustrated one of my harp teachers, who was annoyed that I could play the pieces when I obviously was not referring to the page in front of me. A couple of people I knew who were long-time music readers found it a real challenge to play from memory without sheets of music set on a stand in front of them. We all had much to learn.

New neural pathways were being formed in my previously unchallenged brain. Eventually skills and intellectual faculties I didn't know I had surfaced and surprised me. I was an average student and always struggled, but I persevered, held my ground, turned in my work and contributed in ways that would have been impossible only a year or so before.

The intensity of study grew steadily over the first year and intensified further at the conclusion of the second year, but the music! Oh, the music we made! It often verged on the divine. It was a privilege to be involved in what we were doing.

The actual work of playing at the bedside for patients didn't come until the second year, and only then when we had proven to our harp and voice teachers that we had mastered and memorised the repertoire required of us, were we allowed to attend bedside musical vigils.

℘

My Chalice mentor and I found our way to the log house set on a small acreage in its leafy out-of-town setting. This was not a quaint little log cabin but a majestic home with huge split-log walls and riverstone chimneys. I assumed the occupants in this home were quite wealthy.

She drew her car to a halt prior to our arrival at the house and we sat in the silence for a time before she spoke.

'I always start this way before a music vigil. Let's just sit and remember why we're here.'

I closed my eyes in the stillness. This was one of my earliest music vigils and I remember how pleasant it was to stop and be still in this way before we made contact with the people who had called for our services. Eventually we broke the silence, started the car engine once more and drove further along the road, turning into their gravelled driveway. We unloaded our two harps and rang the front door bell.

The graceful manner in which my mentor helped the two occupants of this home understand what was to transpire, and the elegant manner in which she played her harp, were two things that stood out for me that day and remain with me still.

This home was beautifully decorated in a tastefully coordinated Montanan theme. Before we left for this vigil, I was told the husband and wife I had now been introduced to had just sold their ranch to their eldest son and had settled into their new home to enjoy retirement. Unfortunately they found out that he had cancer and now had very limited time to live. The tragedy of the situation was obvious to us all.

The conversation was gently directed away from our introductions and turned to the reason we were there. An invitation for them both to lie on the bed together while we played was offered. They looked at one another, paused for a moment, smiled and agreed.

We followed them into their bedroom where they lay down together on a log-post bed, lying separately with their heads on the pillows. Eventually they turned towards each other and held one another in their arms. It was such a tender moment to witness. The affection between them was obvious. For this moment their thoughts of the future did not exist and our presence was barely noticed.

The first harp was set to one side of their bed and I was beckoned to place mine on the opposite side. I was nervous. There had been so much for me to take in even in this short period and now I could feel myself being undermined by my own self-doubt. Would I be able to play well enough?

My teacher played first, lightly touching the strings of her harp while focusing her gaze on the entwined couple in front of us. Her music was gentle and beautiful. Her hands caressed the strings so elegantly as she continued playing, bringing more and more sound into the room. She looked towards me, perceived my uncertainty, and with smiling, kindly eyes indicated that I should join her by playing my harp too. She waited for me to join in but then mouthed the word *Sing?* indicating a question with her eyes and smiling. I immediately felt reassured, for she knew singing was my stronger skill.

She then began to sing as she played. It was a familiar piece we both knew and one I had learnt during my training. I joined her, singing the melody just using vowel sounds as she was. She waited and allowed our voices to find a comfortable union. Then she indicated with an upturned look that perhaps I could offer some harmony. I did and the male and female qualities of our voices combined in an ancient chant of adoration.

On reflection afterwards I realised we were in fact mirroring in song the intimate scene playing out in front of us. The choice of music, the lack of words and the way it was being offered was no accident. This offering was prescribed. I knew I was in the company of a true teacher.

About thirty minutes into our vigil the husband drifted off into a very deep sleep. His wife looked at us and smiled, lay there for a while longer with her eyes closed, then gradually and carefully unfolded herself from his arms. The three of us tiptoed quietly from the room. In the kitchen we accepted her heartfelt thanks and the hugs but declined an offer of coffee. We gathered our harps together as seamlessly as possible and made our way back to the car.

My mentor drove off but then parked a hundred metres or so down the driveway away from the house. 'Let's just sit again in the silence and reflect,' she said. 'Just allow any images and thoughts to rise. There's so much that happens in a vigil it's as if all time is compressed into those few special moments. We seem to move into a different time frame from the one we experience in our day-to-day lives. Often in silent reflection, the reason becomes clearer for choosing to play what we did in that moment, and we become more aware of the subtle clues we responded to. Only then, when you've allowed the silence to speak to you, should you attempt to record anything on paper for your class vigil discussions. Try not to use your logical thinking process, but just allow the silence to speak to you.'

As we sat in the silence once again, I immediately felt the tension I was holding within myself. I let it go with a long and hopefully inaudible sigh. Then for some reason images of the house came to me: the tanned, split logs and the colour of bedspreads and coordinating pillows. But then I remembered the smile that passed between the couple at my mentor's suggestion of playing for them in their bedroom. I saw in my mind's eye the pale, slightly strained face of the strong man we had just met who had been keeping up the appearance of joviality on our arrival. I saw clearly my mentor's elegant hands caressing the strings and knew I wanted to emulate that gentleness and elegance in my playing.

At that stage I could only guess at the reasons she had chosen to play the pieces she did, and I waited until questions were invited about the session's music choices on the drive home.

I learnt so much in that early musical vigil and I was all too aware I still had much to learn.

By observation and reflection over the next eleven months, as I attended the required sixty-five end-of-life music vigils, I learned to apply music in a very special way. This was not just the playing of lovely background music or the offering of favourite tunes to entertain.

We were taught how to offer musical pieces in order to minister to the person in front of us. To help them to breathe differently, helping them to deal with the pain they were enduring, and more. We were taught to help them feel confident enough to rest into the music and let go into a deep peace. We learnt how to intuit and act on the subtleties that we eventually became able to perceive. These were major clues to the way we were to be in a vigil. The subtleties informed us of the way we were to play, and what we were to play from our repertoire. When to sing, when not to sing, when to do nothing but remain in the profound stillness and peace that arrives unannounced during the breaks between our offering of music and song. This movement from sound into silence was the constant theme of our work. The profound silence we engendered through our playing was the desired destination at the bedside of patients. Silence was a place in which to rest, a place in which to find solace and comfort, a place in which to surrender. The interplay between music and silence is often the catalyst for a profoundly beautiful and sacred experience. The vigils for me were the culminating high point of all our studies.

Mid one morning I was surprised to receive a phone call from Therese asking me to come to her office. I wondered if this was ominous and made the appointment for later that afternoon, wondering what might be wrong.

'Let me play you something, Peter. You may not have heard this before.'

She pressed a button on her player and I immediately recognised the piece I was hearing. It was 'Call to Prayer' from *African Sanctus* by the composer David Fanshawe. I knew it because I had brought a tape recording of that particular piece with me from Australia. Also on the tape were Coleman Barks' reading of Rumi's 'Reed Flute Song' and a few other favourites of mine.

'I think I may have heard it before,' I said, not wishing to take away her surprise.

'Peter, I want you to sing this at our graduation ceremony and I wanted you to know beforehand. I believe you're capable of doing it. Our musical director will help you and the choir will be there with you singing their part. I believe you can do it. Do you think you can? Would you like to?'

Would I like to! Back in Australia I had found this track on an LP I had borrowed from the Geelong library. This was during my time of questioning and searching and when I heard it for the first time I was moved to tears to hear this field recording from Cairo of an African muezzin calling people to their daily prayers. David Fanshawe had composed a mass with a Christian Kyrie for a choir to sing in conjunction with this Islamic piece. His music took ecumenism to a creative new level by intertwining the two faiths in sung prayer.

The call to prayer was not a simple song. It was pitched at the highest extreme of my vocal register and required me to find this high note right from the very first moment I uttered a sound. It asked for confidence and full commitment. The song was also sung in Arabic, a language I had no experience of. For millions of people in the Islamic world this was a familiar call to evening prayer and was from a religion I knew very little about.

℘

When we came to the first practice with our choir I was nervous on many counts. So much so that when the choir sang their long introduction I couldn't even commit to singing the first note at the high pitch that was required of me. It took a lot of courage and many false starts for me to even be able to commit to making a sound.

Back at home I listened time and time again to the recording I had brought with me, trying to emulate the language and the call. To some degree I was able to, but I also became concerned that we were using a song from a spiritual tradition that wasn't mine. I wanted to know if I was walking over another person's sacred ground. I wanted to talk to an Islamic cleric about it, one who could give me permission to sing the prayer. I couldn't find one in Missoula at all.

After much searching over several weeks, one day my eyes fell upon my ney, the instrument I had brought with me from Australia. The ney had Islamic and Sufi connections, and I wondered if perhaps someone who knew about the ney would be able to help me. I then remembered a conversation I had had with Andy Rigby, my harp-making friend from Australia, before I left. He told me of a fellow harp builder he met on one of his trips to the States whose name was Arsalaan. Andy noticed that Arsalaan carried what looked like a flute-sized wooden box with him wherever he went. Andy, being a flautist himself, asked Arsalaan what it was he had in the box. He had opened it to reveal two reed neys. Andy for some reason thought I would be interested to know about him and had given me his phone number, 'Just in case.'

I found the number, took a chance and phoned him. When I explained my reason for my call Arsalaan and I fell into conversation. He was a friendly person and was interested in my quest.

'Why not come over to Boston and I'll introduce you to some people who may be able to help. In fact, we're having a Sufi retreat at a ski lodge this summer. You could join us if you like. There'll be a group from Turkey and some nice people to meet; in fact one of the clerics is planning to teach the call to prayer. If you came to Boston, we could drive there together and share the travelling costs. I'll send you a brochure.'

I couldn't believe my luck. Here was the chance of a lifetime and the opportunity to know more about the Sufis I was fascinated by and to learn the chant I was to sing at our graduation.

I didn't know how I could afford to go or if I could leave Jeanette and the girls at all for the four days of the retreat. During the next two weeks I sold a couple of my own didgeridoos, which gave me the extra money to use. Jeanette was pleased for me to have the opportunity to go and encouraged me to apply. The die was cast.

The brochure I received called for anyone who had a gift to offer by way of music, or a workshop, to submit the suggestion to the organisers for consideration for the retreat. I offered a didgeridoo-making workshop for the children and didge lessons for anyone who was interested. They were pleased with my offer and accepted.

I eventually flew into Boston to meet Arsalaan's friends. They turned out to be a warm, friendly, fun-loving bunch on a sincere spiritual quest. I liked them enormously. Amongst the people was a group from Turkey and one of them was a master of traditional Turkish instruments. These people were lovers of Rumi, as was I, and I found out that several were Mevlevis, the whirling dervishes I had read about.

In a barn one night in the Vermont countryside, as we sat on the floor and watched the Sema, the whirling ceremony, unfold, I found out that Arsalaan was their principal ney player.

We shared music and stories, I taught the children the didgeridoo, we walked in the wooded mountain tracks and spent time together talking, the conversations usually turning to those of a spiritual nature . . . and I learned the call to prayer and was given permission to use it. I was told that the original singer of the call, Bilaal, was an outsider and when asked to call the attention of a large group of people for prayer, this is what he sang. For centuries, five times a day, a call like this is used to bring millions of worshippers to their knees in prayer.

I sang the call at our graduation in the company of my classmates, who were the choir. They were wonderful and the drama of it was a stunning moment in our graduation ceremony.

The required commitment to immediately reach the high notes in this chant means that as the singer I cannot hold back. It is as if I am stepping off a cliff and hoping I can still fly. Because of the emotional intensity and the amount of breath required I also experience a physical high when I finish. We eventually recorded it as the closing piece on a CD that we made.

In Australia I am sometimes asked to perform the piece at special events. Perhaps I am oversensitive about it, but if a Muslim cleric is present I will always defer the singing of it to him and I will only sing if people are open to it and appreciate the nature of the piece.

14

B'

Adventures of Spirit

Quite separate from the growing intensity of our training, we did find time to enjoy our time as a class, as a family, and individually.

One of our classmates, Sylvia, lived on an acreage in the woods within the nearby Indian reservation. Along with all of my classmates, we visited her property several times, enjoying being together sharing stories or just walking silently alongside the fast-flowing streams and through the forest to hear the sound of the wind swishing through the pines. During these times we came to know each other well and, naturally, there was always music. At every occasion people brought their instruments and we sang, drummed, danced and played our harps together.

In our first weeks in Missoula I came across a sign on a church noticeboard: *Dances of Universal Peace. All Visitors are Welcome.*

I encouraged Jeanette to attend with me, and one night later that week we followed the sound of music into a church hall. A guitarist and a drummer were standing in the centre of two inner and outer circles of people who were chanting simple songs and moving in time to the music, all the while looking deeply into each other's eyes as they sang.

Jeanette and I looked at each other, took a chance and entered into the spirit of the occasion. We joined the circle and found ourselves returning the caring gaze of openhearted companions.

During a break we chatted to the participants, who of course noticed our Australian accents. Conversations turned to the reason for us being in Missoula, and to music. In passing someone mentioned the didgeridoo and I explained that I played the instrument and had brought one with me.

One of the members pricked up his ears at hearing this. 'Wow!' he said. 'You must play for us at our big event at the University Ballroom soon. We've invited Coleman Barks to read a selection of Rumi's poems and he always likes musicians to back him as he reads. Will you play your didgeridoo with them?'

Coleman Barks? Was I hearing correctly? This was the Coleman Barks on the tape I had borrowed from Noor in the Spiral Bookshop back in Melbourne. Hearing his reading of this poetry along with the ney, frame drum and oud had been pivotal factors in turning my life around not so long ago.

Three weeks later I found myself on stage at the University Ballroom with a group of wonderfully skilled, intuitive musicians from Missoula whose task it was to create the mood appropriate to each of Rumi's poems read at random by Coleman from his collection. What a privilege it was for me to be there, playing and singing with them.

At one point Coleman read this poem by Rumi:

Today like every other day, we wake up empty and frightened.
Don't open the door to the study and begin reading.

Take down a musical instrument.
Let the beauty we love be what we do.
There are hundreds of ways to kneel and kiss the ground.

He repeated:

Take down a musical instrument.
Let the beauty we love be what we do . . .

'Play your didgeridoo, Peter Roberts,' he said.

Let the beauty you love be what you do.
There are hundreds of ways to kneel and kiss the ground.

Standing in that ballroom on stage with Coleman and the musicians, being a part of the creative, contemplative, prayerful offering, meant more to me than anyone could ever know.

From that day on I was 'that Aussie didgeridoo guy'. People in Missoula had never come across the instrument up close before. I had the Aussie accent, I played the didge therefore I must be an expert. Right? Well, not quite. I felt that my didgeridoo-playing was average in comparison to the real didge players I knew but I went along with it anyway.

My presumed didgeridoo-playing excellence and authoritative knowledge took me to some fascinating places, such as the University of Montana as guest lecturer in their world music class. I was also interviewed on a Native American TV program that was broadcast through the Indian reservations and up into Canada. I ran didgeridoo workshops in the local music store, I demonstrated the instrument and told dreamtime stories of its creation in schools, and I also gave private lessons. But I did have a real need to make a living and so

I sold off most of my own didge collection to those who were interested.

The geographical location of Missoula, with its streams, nearby mountains and the distinctive contrasts in weather were the catalyst for marvellous outdoor activities as well. In summer Jeanette, Katherine and Ellise were invited by several of the women from our Chalice class to join them on a river float. This event was a summer ritual for many of the locals. It consisted of placing truck or tractor tyre inner tubes into a fast-flowing river a couple of miles upstream, clambering aboard and letting the current float the tubes back downstream. They drifted past fields in the sun, then underneath overhanging trees and back out into the sun. They were at the mercy of the river as it took them into small, fast-flowing rapids that crossed clear, shallow water and sometimes into the deeper parts of the river.

Jeanette still remembers the sound of the water in the shallows as it flowed over the rocks. This simple, natural outdoor activity in the company of close women friends was one of many very fond memories for her.

Our girls settled into their schools and made new friends. Katherine soon went on to attend the University of Montana and to live on campus. In the winter they were able to go skiing in the mountains and tramping through the snowfields. I remember Ellise meeting friends at an ice-skating rink in town that we discovered had been a football field and was now flooded with water. The water had frozen to form an improvised, floodlit, outdoor skating rink.

In early winter we travelled to a natural hot springs situated in the forest to enjoy soaking in the warm pool as snow fell around us. There were very few people there and as Jeanette, Katherine and Ellise soaked in the pool's muddy warmth, a moose graced their company with its presence, wandering nearby without even noticing them. The experience and views were virtually unspoilt. That is, until a man close by stood up to towel himself dry. The girls couldn't believe what they saw. He was totally naked! My young daughters were given a view of natural life they weren't expecting. They laughed about it on the way home and at the memory of it even now.

Such was life in Missoula. We miss those times still after all these years.

As we had no working visa, we were forced to draw on our savings and from my superannuation fund. We did whatever else we could to create some sort of supplementary income. Jeanette did some babysitting, we did private gardening work together, and we shovelled snow from a local business sidewalk each week for money. And of course I sold my didges.

Jeanette had her own interests. She learned to play the harp from one of my teachers and completed a yearlong massage therapy and healing arts course. She also volunteered her services at St Patrick Hospital, where I was training. The volunteer team was large and provided a much-needed and respected service. As a nurse, Jeanette was familiar with hospital routine and her task at this place was to accompany the new arrivals to their rooms and help them settle in. She also accompanied those who were leaving hospital back to their vehicles, making sure they were safe.

During her time at the hospital she met a fellow volunteer named Dave. He had been a lawyer and had fallen on hard times through trying circumstances. He told Jeanette about a Native American tribe who helped him through his difficulties when no one else could. Miraculous events occurred for Dave around issues of health that he couldn't explain and he became very close to these Native American people who adopted him.

Jeanette shared Dave's story with me, and of course I was keen to meet him.

A month or so later Dave invited us both to join him and his partner Kathy on a road trip to the 'res', the Indian reservation where his adopted family lived. We couldn't pass the opportunity by. We borrowed a tent and a few camping provisions and one weekend left for an unknown destination, driving in tandem behind Dave and Kathy's large and very old Chevrolet.

We drove for hours and hours, following Dave to Havre, a small dot on the map in northern Montana up towards the Canadian border. Many of the houses and yards we passed in the reservation were weary-looking and unmaintained. Driving further beyond the towns we eventually came to a small house in an open field where a number of pickup trucks and cars were parked. We turned off our engines and parked ours then followed Dave into the house.

The Native American people in this house were quiet and undemonstrative towards us so we stayed in the background as Dave spoke to them, explaining who we were. Eyes looked toward us and back again to Dave. No one spoke.

It was eventually accepted that we were Dave's friends and our being there was permitted. The reason everyone had come this day was to participate in a community 'sweat'. A sweatlodge had been built in the yard and all present were there to be cleansed. We didn't know it at the time but the cleansing was in preparation for a sundance, an important three-day ceremony to be held several weeks later.

Eventually the men filed outdoors from the house towards the dome-shaped sweatlodge. The women remained in the house as clothes were being shed and men donned shorts or bathing costumes. Among the men there were jokes and friendly banter about how fat some of them had become, but the good-natured fun belied the seriousness of their intent. This was preparation for a sacred ceremony.

I borrowed some shorts and tried to be friendly with anyone who looked my way but I knew I was the outsider. There were many unspoken rituals I had to learn by observation for no one explained them. It was a lesson for me in awareness and humility. I learned by mistake that there was only one direction you should walk around the fire. I discovered that there were people of distinction among the group who required a degree of respect. Distinctions related to age and status in the community.

Joe Ironman, their medicine man, led the sweat. Joe was a big man and also the local policeman. The men deferred to him without question. I found out that I needed to ask Joe's permission in quite a formal manner before I could attend his sweatlodge. All men did. It took the overcoming of nerves and honest self-questioning in order to be able to look this stern man in the eye, to give him a reason for my presence, and to humbly ask his permission to join his lodge. Was I just doing this for an adventure or to have something to tell the people back home?

I dug deeper within and found my reason. Along with the request to join the sweat was the required tobacco offering. I offered mine to Joe and told him my reasons for being there. He looked into my eyes deeply for a time without speaking. Eventually he accepted my tobacco offering and agreed to allow me to join them.

The first men ready to enter had lifted the flap covering the small opening into the sweatlodge. On Joe's command we entered. All the men sat to one side and eventually the women arrived wearing modestly cut cotton-sheet dresses. They sat opposite. The fabric flap door was closed and we were now in total darkness. Hot rocks had been placed in a pit at our feet, and being close to the edge of the pit I could feel the fierce heat radiating upwards, towards me.

We were crushed together and it became hotter and stuffier by the minute. Joe threw water on the rocks in the pit and a gush of hissing steam filled the lodge and our lungs.

Then the sound of chanting began, led by Joe: 'Hey ya ya ya ya. Hey ya ya ya ya. Hey hey ya ya ya.'

Others joined him once he had established the chant. It was a call to the grandfathers, their ancestors who were guiding their lives. The heat from the number of bodies, the steam and the noise of the chanting were almost unbearable but it continued on and on. I started to wonder how I would ever get through it. I couldn't see Jeanette at all and wondered how she was faring in the darkness of the women's side of the sweatlodge.

The chanting stopped suddenly and the door covering was flung open. We tumbled out to suck fresh air deeply into our lungs, but this was only the end of our first round. Newly heated rocks from the fire were placed in the pit. We had three more rounds to go.

Somehow Jeanette and I managed to stay the distance and afterwards were relieved to be able to speak with each other and to be finally out in the open air. We were tired but rested and felt refreshed. Apparently now it was time for a celebration and feast and we were invited to join in. We followed the cavalcade of cars to the event.

Jeanette and I pitched our small, two-man tent near the community hall where the celebrations had begun. The drumming and shrill high-pitched chanting was electrifying. Inside the hall a dancing competition was concluding but the dancers were still tiptoeing lightly on their moccasined feet. Their deerskin beaded costumes jangled and tossed from side to side, and their feathers and braided hair flew freely about to the rhythms of the drums. The hall was alive with amazing sights and wild sounds.

My attraction to the Native American artefacts in the Spiral Bookshop in Melbourne surely was a foretaste of our good fortune in being here.

I could write pages on the events that followed: the sage-smoke cleansing of everyone and everything that entered the building; the hushed entrance of Tatunka; the sacred buffalo totem being carried in by a tearful Joe Ironman; the huge, shared feast; the smoking of prayer pipes being reverentially passed around; the group of drummers who sat ready to play the upturned buffalo-skin drum in preparation for the chant.

At one stage of the evening I was called from where I was standing to come and drum with the men. Had I misunderstood? No, they wanted me to cross the hall and join them.

As I took my place on the floor among the drummers I gratefully took the prayer pipe passed to me. I drew on it and passed it on to the man beside me, having first held it upwards to acknowledge each of the four directions as the others had done. The chant began again and we beat in unison on the hard, upturned buffalo skin to the rhythm of the rattles, singing song after song. We drummed and sang for hours.

Later that night as Jeanette and I cuddled together in our cosy little tent, we had to pinch ourselves. Did the events of this day really happen? Were we actually here? We eventually drifted to sleep to the sound of drumming and singing in the distance.

Two months later we returned. The medicine men had discerned the season and declared that it was now time for the sundance.

Intermittent and heavy thumping sounds woke me from my light sleep. Pelting noisy raindrops hit randomly on the blue tarpaulin I had drawn over my legs. The rain was all I needed to make the night even more memorable. Now I would be weary *and* wet.

I pulled myself even further under the birch branches of my leafy shelter and hoped that these raindrops wouldn't eventuate into something more. The soft birch leaves brushed my cheeks as I leaned forward to see through them into night sky above. I could make out a few dark clouds passing across in front of the moon. Because they were moving quickly I felt reasonably sure the threat of a downpour wouldn't turn into something more. I lay back in my shelter and closed my eyes again, thankful and hopeful. The nearness of the leaves around me and the smell of the dampness of the earth were comforting.

I felt cold and drained. The soft deerskin moccasins I had been given by Dave had already absorbed moisture from the grass that was downtrodden as I danced all through that first night. My feet were wet. I was shivering. The jacket and sleeping bag I had brought weren't warm enough to fend off the cold night.

The drumming had stopped some time before. I wasn't sure how long ago. An hour? Two? We weren't allowed watches or any other belongings from the outside. I couldn't know for certain. All that mattered now was to get through my exhaustion in order to find strength to stand again alongside my Native American companions to dance when the drumming started again.

All through this first day and night we were summonsed by hour after hour of drumming and chanting. Summonsed by Joe Ironman and the tribal elders who sat huddled around their small glowing fire in the growing darkness of our enclosed leafy hideaway.

We had no food, no water. We all danced bare-chested and -legged, covered only at the waist by cotton fabric. Although we did have sleeping bags, I had only a pair of trousers and a jacket with me to cover myself when the drums ceased and was able to duck down behind the leafy shelter for a welcome rest.

Exhaustion was overtaking me and I had two more days and nights to go before the ceremony finished and I would be allowed out into the world I had come from. I wondered just how I could keep going. What on earth was I doing here? Doubts and self-questioning thoughts turned over and over in my foggy mind. What exactly was I doing here in the far north of Montana on this Native American reservation, participating in this sundance ceremony?

I had certainly left the security of home and a familiar reality behind when I left Australia ten months before. Something had drawn me toward making this journey and now these circumstances were taking me deeper into very unfamiliar and uncertain territory. I was scared, tired, worried . . . I felt truly alive and I loved it!

We danced for three days with eagle-bone whistles in our mouths, blowing shrill notes into the sky. Hour after hour of dancing in time to the drumbeat and high-pitched crying chants of the elders. There was nothing to be done but keep our heads up, focus and refocus our attention up into the sky towards the 'eagle nest' branches strung atop of the sacred centre-pole as we supported the sacrificial ritual being conducted in front of us.

Men and women were sacrificing themselves to pain in exchange for prayers being answered: the curing of a mother's cancer, the healing of a sick child, the protection of endangered animals. It was a raw, earthy experience and one that I will never forget.

The sense of relief and feeling of accomplishment at the conclusion of the long hard sundance was overwhelming. I will never forget the hug I received from an elderly Native American woman to thank me for praying this way with them. There was the receiving of gifts in a giveaway ceremony for the sundancers. I was given some blankets, a tobacco pouch and other small items.

There was also a welcome and warm hug from the wife of this Aussie sundancer. Jeanette had spent her few days enjoying being among the wives and children of the Native American families, camping and sleeping in our little tent under the trees in the sacred sundance grounds.

The next year I participated in the sundance ceremony again, but this second time I came to a realisation midway through that this way was not mine and I felt the strong conviction that I should not have been there.

There is so much to tell. Looking back now, I have come to appreciate these experiences as gifts offered to me on my journey towards learning ways for me to forge my own belief systems and discover who I really was.

15

ℛ

Turning toward Home

After two and a half years our adventure in Missoula was over. Our visas and our money had virtually run out and Katherine and Ellise needed to be back in time to begin the school and university year in Australia. Having completed the sixty-five vigils required of me and sat the final two-day exams, I could do no more and we needed to turn towards home.

Returning to Australia was not without worry. From time to time I had received letters from staff members and my business partner at Roberts Interiors. They were troubled letters, full of concern that the business was not going well. I knew, because I withdrew money from time to time, that it was not coming from profit but instead from our growing overdraft. There was nothing I could do about it from so far away. I was not sure what would be in store for me when I got home. I had to put that aside and hope for the best.

It was such a wrench to leave our friends and the warm community of Missoula. We held a huge garage sale and our friends conducted a touching public farewell in honour of the

Roberts family. Carriers were arranged to collect our boxes. One night Jeanette and the girls and I, and a large group of Chalice friends packed fifteen tea chests of belongings to send home to Australia.

It broke our hearts to leave.

Instead of a direct flight home to Australia, Jeanette and I chose to make a visit to my teenage folksinging companion Svein Koningen, who was now living with his wife Dianne in a small village in southern France. This was our chance to have a family holiday before I tackled the uncertainty of making my living as a music-thanatologist back in Australia.

Our flight to Europe would take us across the United States to the east coast, and as I was keen to introduce Jeanette and my daughters to the people I had met at the Sufi retreat a few months back we stopped in Boston, hired a car and drove to Vermont where several members lived.

Hospitality is one of the key traits of those who follow the Sufi path and Jeanette, the girls and I were welcomed wherever we went. We shared meals and accepted an offer of accommodation for our stay in a large, white-painted wooden homestead set amongst the trees in the Vermont countryside. Who would have thought that the sound of a ney, the simple reed instrument that I heard on the tape recording Noor gave me back at the Spiral Bookshop in Australia, would somehow lead us here.

During this visit I had the chance to deepen my connection with these warm people, and Jeanette and the girls were able to share their friendship too. We were taken on scenic drives through the backcountry roads lined either side with trees shedding the last of their colourful autumn leaves. There was ample time for meandering through the charming small towns that dotted the Vermont countryside. All in all it was a satisfying break for us.

We continued our journey home to Australia, stopping for a short time of sightseeing in England, Wales and Ireland, then flew to Nice, hired a car and drove to find Svein in his new digs.

The night we arrived at Svein's home Jeanette and I slept with the louvered windows of our bedroom propped wide open to the clear fresh country air. I awoke to find Jeanette with her chin cupped in her hands, elbows resting on the window ledge and gazing quietly across the terracotta-tiled rooftops of the village. She had slipped from under the covers of our cosy feather doona without waking me and was in her own place of reverie looking at the view below her.

She eventually turned and spoke. 'This is an absolute dream come true.'

I smiled in response and she turned back to the open window. How fortunate we were to be there. We had faced so much together over the last three years and to find ourselves in this place was indeed something to be savoured.

Svein and Dianne had rented a house in La Garde-Freinet, a small medieval village situated high in the hills and this morning was the first of our days together with them. We could hear the sound of chatter, laughter and the clattering of dishes coming from downstairs. Our girls were both awake and were talking to Dianne, who had begun preparation for the Christmas meal we were to have later that afternoon.

It was such a pleasure to be with our Australian friends once again, and here in France of all places. Svein had long harboured a dream of pursuing his passion for painting and had decided to opt out of the world of commerce in Australia to give it a try. Always a man of style, he had thankfully chosen this French village to make his new beginning.

Svein and I once shared a desk in primary school. We had formed a folk duo in our youth and sung together in coffee shops and jazz clubs. Now we had both made major changes midway through our lives and were both forging new directions. The easy company of old friends and the camaraderie of past, shared experiences, coupled with the wonderful new circumstances we were all in, made for a happy time together.

The food was prepared and slowly cooking in the oven so we all took a walk along the cobbled streets of the village, chatting together and taking in the sights. La Garde-Freinet is set high in the hills but is still only about fifteen kilometres from St Tropez and the French Riviera. What a wonderful location Svein had chosen.

Later that evening, over a glass or two of wine bought from a local vineyard roadside stall, Svein and I scoured a map to plan a possible road trip that Jeanette, the girls and I could take. As I ran my finger along the roads on the map I stopped in shocked amazement to see an unexpected but deeply familiar name: Cluny. I had learnt about Cluny in great detail through my studies at The Chalice. The end-of-life rituals conducted by the monks were the inspiration for the Chalice training programme that I had just completed. Our class had been steeped in these rituals and music over the last two and a half years. I was now even able to play and sing many of the Gregorian chants that were sung by the monks at Cluny.

Cluny was the largest cathedral in Europe prior to the creation of St Peter's in Rome, and at its peak in the 12th century the Cluniac monks had established approximately one thousand smaller sister houses across Europe. The Benedictine order was formed here and Cluny is acknowledged as the leader of Western monasticism. The influence of their holistic form of monastic medicine flows through to this day. The enormous cathedral at Cluny was eventually ransacked and, sadly, its grandeur and beauty destroyed, but many of the other Cluniac buildings remain.

One of the rituals I knew of was that at the time of the impending death of a member of their community, the monk caring for them would clap two boards together as a signal. All the monks would drop whatever they were doing, run to the infirmary or cell where their dying brother lay and surround him with the beauty of the sung prayer that is Gregorian chant. I can barely imagine the impact of hundreds of monks standing around the door of a cell, singing their brother home.

Fred Paxton, one of our Chalice lecturers, translated these ritual details and we were required to study them in detail. Therese Schroeder-Sheker was single-minded in her determination to break down the musical attributes of these chants in order to decipher any link their song choices had to any medicinal qualities the music may have imparted.

I certainly knew about Cluny; I just didn't realise how close we were to it and that it may be possible for me to visit the town.

After a few days with Svein and Dianne we eventually said our goodbyes and headed on a meandering road trip towards Burgundy and the township of Cluny.

About twenty kilometres outside the town, I noticed a faded road sign pointing to my right. It read in simple writing: *Taizé Community*. This was another amazing coincidence, for I had no idea Taizé was situated in this area as well. The music of the Taizé community is famous within the contemplative Christian tradition and Jeanette and I had attended several Taizé-styled contemplative services in Australia.

Brother Roger Schultz established the protestant Taizé community in 1940, though the village church they use for worship was built by Cluniac monks in the 12th century.

The church was extended in the late 1950s, and in the early 1970s the rear wall was pulled down and replaced with sliding doors. These doors could then be opened to connect with huge circus-styled tents erected as attachments whenever necessary to accommodate the many thousands of people, both young and old, who flock to Taizé to attend retreats and join the monks in worship.

To cope with the large cross-section of European languages spoken by modern-day pilgrims to Taizé, the brothers developed a form of chant that is quickly learned through its repetition. The effect of singing these beautiful chants over and over gradually envelops the singers who become drawn into a peaceful, worshipful, contemplative space. The cumulative effect of singing these songs within a large group is emotionally moving to the singer and listener alike.

Jeanette and I looked at each other and decided we needed to come back to visit this place if we could.

Driving on to Cluny we spent our first night in a small, private hotel in the centre of town and the next day set about exploring L'Abbeye de Cluny, its museum and the vast grounds. The weather that morning was bitterly cold and somehow during our walking tour we found ourselves separated from the tour group. We didn't mind at all and were now free to roam wherever we chose. We discovered huge stonewalled halls with ribbed, high-vaulted stone ceilings.

In one building Jeanette and I climbed a flight of stairs and came across the amazing spectacle of shards of sunlight streaming through lead-paned windows that fell directly on the doors of the monks' cells near the infirmary, a place that I had only read about during my studies. We took several photos to try to capture the moment and moved on, roaming the grounds and the many cloistered buildings.

We came across a vast stone hall that echoed the sound of our footsteps on the stone floor. I asked Jeanette if we could stand in stillness for a while and we paused together. Jeanette then moved to another room and I just stayed in the silence. I felt a strong urge to sing, and as no one was there I closed my eyes and this furniture retailer from Geelong sang into the emptiness a chant that had been sung by the Cluniac monks seven hundred years or so before.

Of course many people sing ancient music in interesting historical places, but for me it was a significant personal moment. I now had a link to this particular place in France through the Gregorian chants the monks sang to their dying brothers; these beautiful, sung prayers passed down through the centuries that I had been taught in my training and was now singing.

In the foyer of our hotel that evening we found a flyer informing us of the Taizé church service times and early one morning we drove to find the turnoff that led back to Taizé. As we drove our car into the large gravelled car park signed with directions designating parking areas for buses and cars, I was puzzled to find just a car or two other than our own. I thought there would be lines of cars and hundreds of people streaming into the church. Perhaps we had misunderstood the service times. We chose to take a look in the Taizé Community's pottery and gift shop instead, with plans to drive on soon after.

Curiosity got the best of me and I felt I couldn't leave without at least a look inside the church I had heard so much about. It was a pity that we wouldn't be hearing any music.

We all entered through a side door to find three or four couples, some sitting and some reclining on the carpeted wooden floor facing the altar. The church was dimly lit and dozens of candles glowed in the alcoves set on the wall behind the altar. A large icon stood out as a striking feature. We found a spot of our own, and as there were no chairs we reclined on the floor and joined the other people in the quietness.

Once my eyes became accustomed to the dim light, I could see that this was a very simple and well-used space. A wooden walkway ran from the front altar up into the church, dividing it in two. It was fascinating to sit in the semidarkness, just taking everything in.

Then, unannounced, twenty or so white-robed monks entered the building from the left of the altar and in single file walked towards us along the central walkway. They turned around to face the altar again and sat down silently on their haunches or on prayer stools. More silence. Eventually a solo chant was offered into the space. The other monks responded, joining him in song. There was a call and response, a call and response. For the most part I listened, singing quietly to myself when I felt I knew the tune well enough to join them.

Then came a chant familiar to me from the past, the male voices combining and repeating over and over: 'Veni Sancte Spiritus. Veni Sancte Spiritus.' It was an absolutely beautiful moment to have their voices cradling us in their song: 'Veni Sancte Spiritus. Veni Sancte Spiritus.'

Then, as if from another world, a young female soloist joined them, singing from a position far away at the very back of the church. She sang a melody high above the men's low chant. It seemed to me that this young woman was improvising a counter melody. It wove its way in and out and above the monks' voices. It was beautiful and very moving.

Eventually, in conclusion, the singing gently and peacefully faded away into silence. The quietness that ensued afterwards felt so appropriate. The service lasted for approximately forty-five minutes and then, just as they had arrived, the monks left, walking in file silently from the room.

Reflecting on the experience now, I have come to appreciate that the lack of outside participants in the service that I was so keen to see was of no concern to the brothers. I believe they were there to offer their prayers as they had always done, day in and day out, year after year. They weren't singing to entertain or to draw a crowd. Theirs was an offering of praise. Thousands of people are drawn to this little town to experience and share in the beautiful simplicity and sincerity of the sung form it takes.

We travelled further, taking in the scenery of the French countryside knowing that our time was coming to an end. Eventually we caught a series of planes that took us home to Australia, to settle the girls back into school and university, and for all of us to try to reintegrate into our former community.

I had some hard work to do, and quickly. I needed to find a way of offering my new skills with the harp. If I couldn't do that, all the effort and sacrifices we had made over the last two and a half years would have been wasted.

16

Solitary Pioneer

We arrived back in Australia at the start of a long, very hot summer. In the sun's heat, we dragged our suitcases across the road towards the bus terminal, jammed them into the trailer of the waiting minibus and clambered aboard. I looked from my side window to see a row of large, drooping flags on the median strip. 'Welcome to the city of Melbourne' was their limp message. Their flaccid, lacklustre welcome reflected my own low spirits. In that moment I knew I didn't want to be here at all.

The bus pulled away from the kerb and into the traffic. Heading along the highway past the familiar commercial buildings, it then turned away from the city and towards Geelong. The grass in the paddocks along this highway looked bleached and dry, the soil parched and thirsty. It really had been hot.

Tiredness from the long flight overtook me and for the next hour I retreated into a silent world, staring across the flat landscape lost in my own thoughts. Part of me thought hopefully about the future. I remembered a gift my family had given me for my birthday. It was a catalogue of the work of American artist Michael Parkes and within the cover he had signed his name and written a message to me: *Fly high, dream dreams, don't look down, don't look back. The best is yet to come.*

The words reverberated in my mind and were an encouragement, something to hold onto for the future I had worked so hard for. At the same time, another part of me was thinking about what I would find at Roberts Interiors. The letters from home had not grown any more positive. Overwhelmingly, though, I was grieving. Worry over Roberts Interiors was nothing compared to the loss I felt in leaving Missoula. I knew that something of great significance was now over.

Eventually we arrived back home in Geelong, where we were collected and driven to my parents' home to catch up with family again. It was wonderful to see them all. Our girls quickly claimed the telephone and were calling friends to let them know we were home.

Because our English tenants still occupied the home we owned we needed to find somewhere to live as soon as we could. We eventually found and rented a pleasant flat near the girls' former school. We retrieved some of our stored furniture and borrowed the rest. Jeanette set about displaying the possessions we had unpacked and the girls decorated their bedrooms once again. Our familiar objects about the place helped to make the flat feel more like home. We were settling back into Geelong once again.

Because we had supported ourselves on our savings in America for so long, by the time we purchased a secondhand car our finances were grim. As I had feared, Roberts Interiors had failed. Wal was now focused on new directions and business opportunities of his own and I had changed. I now had a new focus to the way I wanted to live and I knew I could never reconsider returning to furniture retailing again in order to help revive our business. Roberts Interiors was no longer a viable financial proposition and so we made the decision to close it down.

Our store's closure was the final chapter of a very long period of my life and the removal of an imagined financial safety net. Wal and I advertised heavily and auctioned off stock, fittings and fixtures. It was so sad to see the beautiful furniture, pictures, lighting and interior items and countless rolls of gorgeous, expensive fabric being sold at auction for a fraction of their cost.

We needed some money to manage the rental of the flat we were in so I made an appointment with the bank to apply for a short-term loan. The young bank manager disregarded our thirty-year history with his bank through Roberts Interiors and L'Amour Gifts. To him I was a mature-aged, unemployed student returning from overseas with a new, very dubious-sounding occupation

'I'm sorry, Mr Roberts, I don't think I quite got that. You're a music-thana . . . thana . . . How do you pronounce that again? I don't know that I've ever heard of it. And what is it that you do exactly?'

He eventually made a decision and turned my loan application down.

I felt frustrated, forced to recognise that my past business history counted for nothing now. I was no longer the well-known businessman from that beautiful furniture store. I was a harpist of sorts with an odd career no one could pronounce.

A week or so later we attempted to purchase a television set at a major discount store on the interest-free terms they had advertised. Again our application was declined. It seems that my credit rating was made available to them through an online credit check system. It felt so humiliating to be in this new, vulnerable position. Now, in my late forties, the reality of having to create a new career path and find a way of making a living at it in the process was becoming all too apparent.

Far from Australia, I had experienced firsthand the beauty and preciousness of the work we were doing. As music-thanatology practitioners, we were held in high regard and felt supported by the community. I was now a long way away from that support and the feeling of security. No one understood.

Many of our close friends listened respectfully to my enthusiasm about playing harp for dying people, hearing me wax lyrical about the beauty of this work. But this was all so unfamiliar to them. It must have been strange for our friends who had known me so well to hear me talking this way: calling myself a harpist and making plans to work in hospitals and hospices with very sick people.

These days I joke that when I returned at least I didn't have my hair in a ponytail or wear a tie-dyed shirt. I wasn't a harp-carrying New Age hippy. In fact I looked pretty much the same as when I left.

Thankfully my friends trusted me and were genuinely interested in the new course I was taking. Other people in the general community had no idea what I was on about; their blank stares told me that. For them I couldn't be placed neatly into a preconceived box of acceptable vocations; therefore there remained an underlying uncertainty around me during many conversations.

As Helen suggested earlier in this book, there still exists in most places an unspoken fear of discussing the subject of death too deeply, and here was I talking about harps and of helping dying people to 'let go' with the help of my music.

A neighbour spread a rumour that I had joined some sort of death cult. Of course there was no truth to this whatsoever, but after all that we given up in order for me to be trained, and all that we as a family had gone through together, I felt deeply hurt to learn this. The feeling of being an outsider and someone to be a little wary of continued in some circles for many years.

Finally we moved back into our spacious and comfortable home and, together, Jeanette and I resumed as normal a life as possible. Ellise by now had returned to her old school and Katherine had been accepted into Melbourne University and had moved to lived on campus.

Somewhere in the midst of this transitional period, I spotted an advertisement for a scheme the Australian government had established to support creative new business ventures. In order to be eligible a person needed to have a good business idea. I didn't read the fine print too closely and showed the advertisement to Jeanette with the thought that we could apply for it. I felt strongly that I could sell my therapeutic-music idea to them. As my career didn't exist anywhere else in Australia, the concept could certainly be seen to be innovative.

I made further enquiries to find the support scheme consisted of social-service payments guaranteed for a year to help a person establish their new venture. Any financial income from the new venture could be kept without it affecting the payment. This seemed like a perfect chance for us to gain some financial support and make a new start.

I put together an outline of my ideas and called it Threshold Music Services. Threshold Music Services had four aims: the offering of music as medicine; education through public speaking; a music-based stress-management program; and the manufacture and sale of harps. Each of these aims had the potential to raise income. The proposal was ambitious, but after a personal interview to explain the finer details our concept was accepted. The only catch to stop this going ahead was the fact that I had never received a social-service payment and the grant wouldn't be possible without it. In short, I had to be on the dole.

The dole, social security, the government unemployment allowance . . . receiving the dole was an option my pride couldn't permit. This came no doubt from a long-held attitude passed from father to son about self-sufficiency, ambition and enterprise. The dole to me was about failure. But now things had changed. We were desperate for income. I swallowed my pride, collected the application papers from Centrelink and took them home to fill in.

Unfortunately for me the Centrelink office was situated directly across the road from our Roberts Interiors building. The day I applied I parked my car in another street and walked swiftly to the front door in the hope that our staff preparing for the auction wouldn't see me through our large display windows. I felt self-conscious and didn't want to be seen by anyone I knew. I also felt completely humbled by the need to be there at all.

We eventually received a phone call with an appointment to discuss our application. A day later we were sitting waiting for our number to be displayed. There it was!

We stood to enter a booth and speak with a very pleasant young clerk who had already looked over our application form. The young man advised some changes to the way we had filled in the form. He emphasised the need to value assets not in light of what we bought them for, as I had done, but in the light of a forced sale with all items spread out on the front lawn and sold in a garage-sale scenario. He looked over my asset figures, re-evaluating them as he went, and was finally content with the details in front of him. It seemed that in view of our current circumstances we were now eligible for the dole.

On reading that our family had been living overseas for a

couple of years, the young man asked out of curiosity where I had worked before I left. Behind him, to the right of his shoulder and across the road, was a sign boldly displayed on a large building with the name P & J Roberts Interiors. A sign on the window read: *Clearance Auction. Closing soon.*

'I used to work in a furniture shop near here,' I told him.

The government support we received for Threshold Music Services that year was a financial lifesaver.

It is hard for me now to look back over the many years of hardship we experienced as Jeanette and I attempted to settle and re-establish ourselves in our new guise. I personally experienced an immense feeling of loneliness and disconnection that lasted for years. At the same time I needed to present a positive exterior to everyone else if I was ever to make anything of this new career.

I remember clearly my fiftieth birthday two months after our return. It was one of those days when the hot northerly wind had been blowing. We drove to Jan Juc beach and I sat on the access steps to the beach just staring at the waves. I was in a mood of dark self-doubt, wondering if the choices I had made and the sacrifices we experienced as a result were far too costly. What had been the point of it all?

Because of the pressure of expending so much energy on my own, forging a new path and holding the tension of creating an income, I suffered emotional burnout on more than one occasion. Not having the company of my classroom friends, the ones who shared a deep appreciation of the value of our music, caused me great sadness. The only way I knew of dealing with the weariness and despondency was to shoulder it and carry on. Though I tried not to show it, my darling wife and perhaps my children could see it in me. Those lonely, dark times I prefer to put behind me now and not look back. Jeanette and I share the secret of our struggles.

I often questioned why I needed to struggle on my own in this way when all the leadings I had received to follow this musical path seemed so certain. Why did I bother to travel across the world to receive the unique training I had? What was the point of changing my life's direction, burning our bridges and leaving everything behind? Why were we given the chance to experience what we had along the way? We had been blessed with so many adventures and gifts, and now this. Why?

I confided my questioning doubts to a friend, a Uniting Church minister. He thought for a while and shared the following insight into my situation. He told me I now knew personally what it was to face loss, to be hurt, to live in uncertainty and to know vulnerability. He knew I had received and brought about deep peace and comfort through music. He explained that the many losses, highs and lows, isolation and intimacy I had experienced, I now carried within.

'Each time you play your music for someone,' he said, 'you bring all these experiences with you into your playing. You are an informed participant in their life experience.'

I think he was correct in many respects. Musical notes can be read and learnt from a musical score, but finding an attitude of truth from which to play can't be learnt in that way. This must come from within. I remembered a Hassidic saying I heard in my training: 'You cannot give what you do not have.' I was certainly finding out what this actually meant.

17

ß'

Breakthrough

Gradually, a curiosity about my use of music in medical-care settings began to grow and invitations started to come my way. I took advantage of every opportunity to speak at conferences and events whenever I could. I gave twenty formal presentations in the first ten months of returning home, travelling beyond Geelong to Melbourne and interstate.

A spotlight was briefly shone on me at these events, but I returned home to experience the isolation of being a lone, struggling music practitioner. It was a continuing cycle of enthusiasm and compliments followed by loneliness and struggle.

I presented a keynote address at the Third International Mind Immunity and Health Conference in the first few months of arriving home. I remember during the conference finding myself on a panel with Patch Adams, 'the clown doctor' made famous by the actor Robin Williams in his film *Patch Adams*.

As I explained the purpose of my music, he joked to the group, 'Harp music for dying people? Why not put on a red nose and pair of wings when you play that thing? You need to cheer those people up.'

I sighed inwardly at his joke and at the amused smiles. I had my work cut out.

My keynote address, however, went very well and I received many positive comments and much interest in what I was proposing. On the last day of the conference we were packed, ready to leave and saying our goodbyes when a man came across to ask if I would consider moving to northern New South Wales to work in a palliative-care organisation he headed. I showed some interest. He was satisfied and planned to speak to his board of management about it as soon as he returned.

Jeanette heard our conversation and looked at me, shaking her head in disbelief. What would come next? What was this new public role her husband was finding himself in? She yearned for a return to a simple, normal life. Unfortunately it wasn't to be. Opportunities continued for me to speak about my work and I felt I had to accept them in order to explore any possibility they may contain for us.

I travelled to Canberra and to several events in South Australia and New South Wales. My harp and I were once flown in a small plane to Wollongong, New South Wales, where I was invited to speak at the Illawarra District Hospice Conference held at the newly established multimillion-dollar Nan Tien Buddhist Temple. Travelling in the small plane from Geelong and arriving at the enormous temple complex was quite an experience. These moves from one world to another became a new pattern.

I spoke to trainee doctors and nurses and gave public lectures in all manner of places. Just prior to leaving Missoula I had received some valuable advice from an oncologist. I had wanted to know how best to convince doctors and those within the medical profession about the value of the work he knew we were offering through our music.

'Don't explain too many of the details of what this is about,' he said. 'Just play your music. This can't be explained rationally. Leave room for the mystery of the experience. After people hear your music they will understand its value, but this time from their own perspective.'

This was good advice for, as time went by, within my presentations I began to take pressure off myself in attempting to explain the hows and whys of music-thanatology: the effects and benefits. Instead of trying to convince people, I began to share the deeper reasons I have for doing the work. Now I also share the circumstances in which my music has been found helpful and the choices I make in offering it. Then I just play.

After playing and allowing time for silence, often a mysterious or 'sacred space' is encountered. People are often emotionally touched by something special within this simple music. Words fall away and explanations are no longer relevant. Applause is never sought or encouraged at these times; the profound silence is applause enough.

Arriving at this experience is at the heart of a music-thanatology offering.

Through new associations I was now making I met Joy Nugent, founder of the NurseLink Foundation in Adelaide. I found Joy to be a visionary and progressive palliative-care practitioner. Through Joy I was invited to speak at a volunteer's trainee program and fundraising event for the Sandakan Hospice in Malaysia. We arrived as visiting celebrities and were treated accordingly. The community support and fundraising ability this small hospice group had gathered around them was extraordinary.

I was at last beginning to make inroads as a bedside music practitioner and I received a growing number of requests to play for individuals. I travelled to the outskirts of Melbourne to play in private homes. I played for people in nursing homes, hospitals and psychiatric facilities, and also for special-needs support groups. I played for dying children and for sick and frail elderly patients. Whenever I received an invitation, for the most part I accepted.

In America patients were never charged for the music-thanatologist's services. Instead, hospitals, hospices and other care facilities contributed financially to an umbrella fund that compensated the Chalice music-thanatology organisation for their practitioners' time. Those who received a music-thanatology offering understood it to be a gift from their community. This to me was an inspirational concept and one I wanted to follow. I choose not to charge for my services either.

I often told families, 'This is a gift to you from someone in the community,' or 'I receive donations to support this work.'

I hadn't; the donation was always mine. I always presumed hospitals and other care providers would quickly appreciate and embrace this ideal and contribute accordingly, but I was very wrong. To this day, I have never charged patients or families for my palliative-care services. This of course has been a disastrous way to support a family and pay the bills. Some people today still think I sold my business and retired in order to do this work, just as an interest. They will never know how far they are from the truth.

In the very early days after we returned I received almost as many enquiries about harps as I did about the real bedside music work I was offering. Being a businessman in need of an income, I saw this as a business opportunity and set about filling the need. I imported harps to sell. I purchased plans and had a local cabinetmaker manufacture components for me that I assembled, polished and strung in my workshop. I began to teach the harp to those I had sold harps to, and as a result gathered around me an enthusiastic harp community that came to our place to meet regularly for lessons and harp gatherings. We amused ourselves by calling ourselves the Geelong Harp Orchestra. The harp-building arm of Threshold Music Services was another financial lifesaver.

Then I started to make recordings. After meeting at the Mind Immunity and Health Conference I was approached by Ian Gawler, the well-known Australian cancer-support specialist and meditation leader. Ian suggested we should make a recording together in which I would play my music and he would lead listeners in guided meditation. Our resulting CD was called *From Sound into Silence: Meditations with Harp and Voice*. This proved to be a fine combination, and Ian and I have shared many music and meditation-related events and projects together over the years.

I made another recording, this time with Dr Charles Parker, called *Quiet Waters By: For Those Who Walk With Grief*. Charles and I created it as a resource for people being challenged by circumstances of loss. Charles read the selected poems and readings tenderly while I played the harp, flute and sang. We both enjoyed the experience of creating this together, the outcome satisfying to us and well received by those for whom it was made.

People began to question why I hadn't produced a solo recording of my own by this stage, a solo CD of just my harp music. The main reason was that I knew the power of a music-thanatology offering lay in the healing, interactive relationship created between the practitioner and the patient.

This relationship is engendered through a caring presence but also through a continually adjusted, live musical offering. I felt certain that music on a CD could never offer the same result.

A solo recording did come about, however, through the influence of Dr Rosemary Selkirk. Rosemary, a psychologist, had heard me speak and play at the Mind Immunity Health Conference and felt there was a healing quality to my music. She knew my approach was to use live music for individuals but felt there may also be a place for people to be helped through my recorded music.

After three years of asking if I had made my own CD, Rosemary decided that, left to me, it would never happen. She phoned me to say that she had made some enquiries and if I would accept she would both book and pay for a recording studio for me. It seemed that fate in the guise of Rosemary Selkirk was leading me like a reluctant puppy, by the scruff of my neck, to the recording studio to produce something of my own. To this day I remain grateful to Rosemary for taking this initiative as, more likely than not, I would never have produced that CD.

One morning during the planning for this new solo recording, I awoke with the word 'ferryman' going through my mind. Why the word ferryman? I had no idea.

The word stayed with me throughout the morning, and later that day in my barn I sat at my harp and began to play. A flow of music started to develop in response to the word. The music evoked the imaginative scenario that is depicted in the first pages of this book. In my mind there was a young woman being mysteriously and urgently drawn to a voice calling from within. As she travelled, searching for its source, she became prevented from moving closer to it by a vast stretch of water. At the water's edge she came across a boatman waiting for her.

He knew she would arrive and was waiting to take her across. He was a ferryman, and as she was to discover, also the one calling her. He was the source of her yearning. They both embarked on their journey across the water and disappeared into a mist that had fallen. The tempo of the piece is slow and steady with the feeling of oars being drawn strongly and rhythmically through water.

This sounds overly romantic, mushy and fanciful I know, but if you ever have the chance to sit with these images and hear the music being played I'm sure you will appreciate it to be more than a silly notion within a pleasant harp tune. Sometimes now in bedside musical vigils it feels appropriate to play this piece I call 'The Ferryman'. The unspoken notion of being carried home expressed through the rhythm of the music can be quite powerful and of great comfort to the listener. I don't usually sing the words or speak about them at all; however, the images within the story are in my mind as I play.

The ferryman in my piece has nothing to do with the dark, archetypal ferryman figure that Helen was imagining when she came across my music for the first time: Charon, who carries people across the River Styx. My ferryman is a comforting and longed-for lover in the form of a boatman. He is also the source of longing for the woman in my composition. I have since come to appreciate that my 'Ferryman' piece can also be understood as a spiritual love story of yearning and union with one's beloved.

It was wonderful to now have a solo CD to showcase one side of my music.

I remain proud of this composition still. I recorded it first on *Love and the Ferryman*, the solo CD I was making, but I have recorded it since on another CD called *The Sanctuary*. As mentioned previously, the power of a live musical interaction always seemed to me to be an extremely important element in what I offer.

In recording *The Sanctuary* I attempted to bring something of this into the studio and asked a friend to join me when I recorded. She lay on the floor on large cushions and covered herself with a warm doona. I felt for the first time that I was able to completely ignore studio microphones and just play for her. I believe something of this is captured in the recording of *The Sanctuary* and many people have attested to the importance of this recording to them.

As a music-thanatology practitioner, though, my music at the bedside is always played live on a one-to-one basis. Sometimes I choose a familiar piece of music as an entrée to a deeper level of rapport, the same as you would in a conversation with a stranger; it is often appropriate to begin on common ground before you venture further together. I use the elements of music – tempo, timbre, rhythm, melody, repetition, even silence, anything I can draw on – to assist the person in front of me. I leave conversation behind as soon as possible.

Caring, prayerful intentions are carried to the inner realms of the heart and psyche in the musical offering. The use of a prominent melody can attract a person's attention, and once the mind is engaged the melody can then be simplified to help quieten it. The use of rhythm can assist a person to breathe more easily. The modal form of a piece has its part to play in drawing the two of us into relationship further. A deep peace can arrive as we depart from metered time, for we often lose all sense of day-to-day time and enter into a mysterious and welcome encounter with silence as all melds into the moment.

These experiences are so hard to describe and understand, as the spoken language for me has many limitations. As the

American oncologist said, 'Just play your music.' And that's what I do.

Over the years I offered private vigils for people whenever they asked but I always knew a better use of my time and resources would be to find a permanent position within a hospital. I was already playing within hospitals for their patients, but at my own expense. I needed to find another way.

Within the public hospital in Geelong several staff members were keen to have me play for their patients. One enterprising social worker made a request to the hospital foundation that I be employed. Staff members within the foundation advised her that it would never happen; there were simply too many other pressing needs. Ever tenacious, she then applied independently for a grant from the Geelong Hospice Foundation and was successful.

Thanks to the Foundation's generosity she received a sum large enough to pay for my services one day a week for a year. The money was held in trust and earmarked for my services. I was able to play in the oncology wards and for patients receiving chemotherapy. I played for those who were dying and those struggling with the difficulty of treatment. I became a musical fixture one day a week in these areas, playing for people wherever I was referred.

At the end of the year my funding was exhausted and I couldn't afford to continue unfinanced despite the positive outcomes I was having and the relationships being formed. The hospital still had no funding for a therapeutic harp practitioner and so I applied to the Geelong Hospice Foundation myself for an extension of funding and was successful again. I continued playing and extended my services to include regular visits to the hospital's McKellar Palliative Care Unit on another campus.

Through funding from other sources I was able to extend that service for a few more years. These days the McKellar Palliative Care Unit has committed to contracting my services using their own finances and as a result our association has been able to continue.

I am often asked to play at hospital memorial services and other services held for community support groups and I have done so in most cases in an unpaid capacity. In the early days, having accepted invitations to memorial services at St John of God Hospital Geelong, I found an ally in a former head of pastoral services within the hospital. She appreciated the significance of the emotional and spiritual support I was offering through my music and could see ways it could be used within the wards of the hospital.

One of the pillars of the mission of St John of God Hospital is the extension of care beyond the patient's physical needs to assist their healing. The hospital embraces the need to care for a patient's emotional and spiritual needs as well. This leader saw in my music an example of the holistic care the hospital espoused. She tried to exert influence on my behalf, but then left the hospital for another position.

Fortunately I had a similar response to my music from the incoming head of pastoral services and director of mission. In Patricia Boom I had indeed found a mover and shaker as an ally. Patricia proposed that we put a case to the hospital's CEO to explain the ways my music could benefit them in enhancing their offering of holistic care.

I carefully prepared my presentation but I also had a brainwave. I approached two well-known and successful Geelong businessmen to ask if they would be prepared to donate a sum of money, earmarked for my services, to the hospital. I reasoned that they would also be able to claim the donation as a tax deduction. They both knew me and fortunately both agreed.

When I gave my presentation, I outlined my training and experience and as many holistic benefits as I could think of, and then as a concluding statement I was able to say, 'Oh, and by the way I also have found funding enough for a three-month trial period.'

I don't know if that helped but the presentation was successful and the executive agreed to the trial.

That initial three-month trial marked the beginning of my long association with St John of God Hospital. My time on a part-time contract extended for several years and eventually I was appointed as a permanent part-time member of staff attached to the Pastoral Service Department.

Those years spent struggling to find enough work to make a living were challenging. In fact, not just challenging but downright difficult. Nine years later I founded a non-profit charity I called the Institute of Music in Medicine (IMIM). Through IMIM I was able to approach benevolent foundations for donations to support and extend the music-thanatology services I had been offering and self-funding for so long. At the wrong end of my career I had finally created a practical way to receive remuneration for my music at the bedside without adding a financial burden on those for whom I played.

Prior to the foundation of IMIM several people and groups had donated money directly to me, while others made donations to hospitals specifically for my work. I was not informed that these donations had been made, though, and this became a problem for me.

There was one occasion when I was playing in a patient's room and she turned to her husband and asked if he had remembered to donate the money that they had spoken about to the hospital for my services. He said he had. I feigned knowledge of this and thanked them, but it troubled me greatly that if she had not asked that question I would never have known and I would not have had the opportunity to say thank you. I wondered how often this had happened and who among the people I knew went unthanked.

One day my mobile phone rang and at the other end of the line was an English gentleman enquiring if I was the Peter Roberts who plays music for patients in hospitals receiving palliative care. After clarifying that he was speaking to the correct person, he went on to tell me he had been searching for me for some time. He reminded me that several years back we had spoken to each other in a lift at the Alfred Hospital in Melbourne. He had heard me playing my music in a room near the one his wife was occupying and by chance had met me in the elevator as we were both leaving. Now he was enquiring if it would be possible to make an appointment to visit as he had something to offer me. I was intrigued by the call and of course agreed, wondering what it was all about.

We eventually met in Geelong and during our conversation he told me his wife had died from her illness back then and he had established a charitable foundation in her memory. He had remembered our encounter and made enquiries about me. He was touched by what I was doing and wanted to offer me a donation to assist me to grow in my endeavours. He told me he had an amount of fifteen thousand dollars to give to me.

I was overwhelmed by this unexpected kindness and could have kissed him then and there. I do know that I hugged this gentle and kindly Englishman outside in the street as he made preparations to leave.

The intention of his Grenet Foundation was to offer seed

funding to small organisations that were struggling to obtain money to support their work and that otherwise might be overlooked by the larger philanthropic trusts. The funding was to help people like myself to establish and grow.

The one thing he did hope for was the ability to claim a tax deduction for this donation if it was at all possible. He told me businesses and philanthropic organisations all seek this tax advantage in order for their funding to go further. It dawned on me then that this was the reason I had had so much difficulty receiving financial support in the past. I puzzled over how I could manage this for him, and then friends heading another charitable organisation in Geelong agreed that they could process the donation for me. They put the funds in trust to be used specifically for my services within palliative care.

My donor encouraged me to find a way of establishing a non-profit charity of my own. I explored the possibility with a number of law firms, being passed from one to the other until finally one informed me that I would never be able to afford their services because of the many months of work involved. Other people tried to help me but the challenges of my establishing something like this are too long a story to tell.

In the end I did have some good fortune. By chance John Hall, the man who purchased our car before we left Australia, read an article about me in the *Melbourne Age* newspaper and phoned me to say hello and to offer any support he could. I mentioned my law firm dilemma and he offered to make a few enquiries on my behalf. A few days later he called to say his niece worked for a large law firm in Melbourne that had a section within their company offering assistance to charities. He would make the initial contact.

The short version of this is that in 2004 Blake Dawson Waldren, a prestigious law firm at the top end of Collins Street in Melbourne, took my case. Over the next year and a half they worked on my behalf at no charge. We spent many months dealing with the innumerable details required in setting up a benevolent charitable institution that would comply in every manner with the requirements of the law. It was an enormously time-consuming task and an extremely generous gift to me.

In November 2006 the Institute of Music in Medicine, a non-profit charitable company, was established to promote and support the work of music-thanatology.

John Hall continued to offer assistance in establishing an administrative board and became one of the institute's first board members himself. I sought other members from within the Geelong community and began to seek further donations. The Grenet Foundation had generously made another donation in the year prior and so did other philanthropically minded groups and individuals.

In 2004 I noticed an advertisement in the newspaper announcing a scholarship available through Kings Australia, a Geelong-based firm. The scholarship was offered to encourage innovative approaches around end-of-life issues. I showed the details to Dr Sarah Leach, who at the time held a joint appointment between Deakin University School of Nursing and St John of God Hospital, where she was the research and development officer. I suggested we could apply and use the money to research the effect of my music on patients within our hospital.

Sarah contacted her Deakin colleague, Professor Helen Cox, to assist with the preparation of the application form and we became the successful and proud recipients of the inaugural Kings Scholarship, receiving $10,000 for our project. Eventually St John of God, Deakin University and Threshold Music Services supported a two-year music-thanatology research project.

≈

Toward the end of the first year the project money was running out but the project itself was nowhere near finished. In addition, Sarah had resigned from Deakin University and so we were about to have no project leader. Fortunately Helen Cox was about to retire and return to Geelong to live. She offered to take over both the project leadership role and the researcher role in a voluntary capacity.

I had spoken with Helen several times over the telephone as we planned the study and finally met her unofficially at a Meet Your Maker musical instrument and experiential musical presentation I offered within the gorgeous acoustic spaces of the Geelong Art Gallery. That was a brief encounter but we eventually went on to become great friends and spend many months together in this research.

Helen became the hands-on bedside observer and continued the study to completion. She prepared a detailed report for Kings Australia and St John of God Hospital. The report was beautifully written and the contents a wonderful affirmation for me. I shed tears when I read for the first time the many touching stories and outcomes it contained. It dawned on me in the reading of it that this wasn't just a report about therapeutic music in general; it was a report about my music. As a music-thanatologist practitioner, my intention is always to leave patients' rooms as discreetly as possible, leaving little room for conversation afterwards. I had no knowledge of these details outlining the impact my music had been making.

Our music-thanatology research project was the first of its kind in the world. The research was so well written and the outcomes so positive that Helen and I were invited to the prestigious Mayo Clinic in the United States to jointly present its findings at the Mayo Spiritual Care Research Conference in 2006. Presenting in the States in front of the huge conference audience remains a career highlight for me. It seemed I needed this event to accept that perhaps I should no longer think of myself as just a furniture retailer who could play the harp. I was a musician of value in a therapeutic milieu.

Helen and I have shared many vigils together over the years now. She has witnessed firsthand the many intimate encounters shared between patients and myself during my bedside work. As these moments occur it is a comfort to be able to turn to someone who has also witnessed the same moment, someone who shares the significance of the moment. We catch each other's eye in acknowledgement.

We have completed several other projects together, evaluating the effect of my music. One of the most recent and satisfying was the study Helen did in response to funding we received to evaluate the effect of my playing on premature babies in the Special Care Nursery within St John of God Hospital. Helen remains my confidant within the challenges of this work and now also serves as a valued member of the IMIM board.

An Aussie bloke playing a harp in a hospital seems to attract attention and to this day I continue to receive an enormous amount of unsolicited media attention. There have been articles written in local and national newspapers and magazines. There have been featured segments on the radio and television. In 2010 ABC Television presented our journey in their *Australian Story* program titled *Heaven Sent*. The program brought a tsunami of wonderful responses that I have had trouble coping with. Being a solo practitioner with no support staff, I found it a major challenge to cope with the many hundreds of touching letters and requests for help.

For example: Please could you come to Sydney to play for my neighbour's dying children?

Or: Can you possibly play for my dying husband, even over the phone?

Without other trained music-thanatology practitioners to share the load, it is just not possible to respond to so many calls for help.

Among the letters were ninety-three requests from people wanting me to train them! Had I the funding required, such a music-thanatology training program could be established here in Australia, but I have had to learn my limitations and do the best I can with the funding I have and the amount of energy I have to give. However, the resulting offers to speak at conferences, often held in interesting places, has been one of the positive side benefits for both Jeanette and myself.

Somehow nineteen years have passed since I took those first uncertain and seemingly crazy steps towards the musical path I am still on. I was a recipient of the 2008 Tattersall's Award for Enterprise and Achievement and the joint winner of the St Michael's Day Medallion for Outstanding Service to the Community, awarded by Dr Francis Macnab of St Michaels Church in Collins Street, Melbourne. The positive effect of my music has been independently evaluated over the years in separate studies. It seems the path I took may not have been so foolish after all.

These days, while the funding still exists I have more than enough bedside music work to cope with. I still produce harps to sell and now run workshops. One is in the use of the Reverie Harp©, an exciting new therapeutic musical instrument I conceived of and helped to develop a few years ago. I have also produced a new, deeply restful CD of my harp music called *Night Song*, which is creating much interest. I hope to produce a therapeutic music and image DVD in the near future.

The many wonderful things Jeanette and I have experienced, and the places we have travelled together, would never have happened had we not been open to responding to an inner call I felt back then. This call was very strong and deep. I have tried to balance my desire to do this work with the needs of my family and applied myself in the best way I knew how. This I know has often been to the detriment of an appropriate life–work balance.

I can never know the outcome for my daughters and Jeanette had we stayed as we were back then. Jeanette's nature seeks a simpler, less public life. She has shown extraordinary courage in facing the uncharted journey we have taken; yet through it all I have experienced her continued support and encouragement. She too has a story to tell in dealing with her own challenges through all this. My daughters have theirs.

The musical outcomes are whatever they are. I have only set out to be true to something I felt deeply drawing me. I continue to offer my music to the source of that call each time I play.

I rest in the certainty and companionship of that Truth.

Section 3

⁊

Stories of Grace and Sanctuary

Helen

18

Small Mercies

There are countless stories I could tell from the vigils I have personally witnessed, or that people have related to me. In this section I have distilled just a few to illustrate Peter's work. The stories show that this work is precious, that people respond powerfully to it and that it makes a difference.

Nathaniel was a sick little boy and it took a long time – seventy-seven days, to be exact – before he could go home. And even then his future was shaky. Geraldine and Pat, Nathaniel's parents, told me his story.

Nathaniel was born prematurely at thirty-four weeks. He was born with Down syndrome and leukaemia. The Down syndrome was diagnosed around week twenty of the pregnancy. Geraldine had been quite sick and wanted to check on whether the baby was okay. When she discovered the diagnosis she and her husband Pat started actively searching for information that would teach them, prepare them and help then to cope.

She contacted the Down Syndrome Association only to be told that the package they had was given to parents once the baby was born.

'Forget that,' Geraldine said. 'I want it now.'

Her need to be assertive for her little boy started then. She read everything she could get her hands on. 'I felt confident,' she said. 'I felt that I could cope. Little did I know what we were in for.'

The leukaemia was discovered soon after Nathaniel was born with lesions all over his body. That was a shock.

During a pastoral services team meeting, one of the women asked Peter if he would look in on both Geraldine and Nathaniel. They told him about the dual diagnoses and said that it was uncertain whether this little boy would live. Peter had gone to the nursery but picked up that Geraldine wanted privacy, so he played generally in the nursery rather than going specifically to Nathaniel's side. His clear intention for playing, though, was specifically for them.

The next day one of the nurses in the Special Care Nursery was caring for Nathaniel. He was crying and restless and his blood oxygen saturation levels were 'all over the place. Not really low, but quite unstable'. He was not feeding well.

Suddenly she could hear a harp playing and realised that Peter was playing in the birthing suite. As Peter played, she realised that little Nathaniel was responding. He was becoming calmer.

She went to the birthing suite and said to Peter, 'I'm not sure if you have the time, but there's a little boy in the Special Care Nursery who seems to be responding to your music. When you've finished here do you think you could come?'

Peter said he would be there shortly.

Geraldine was not present this time. Peter played while the nurse held Nathaniel. The little boy calmed and settled, eventually going to sleep. His blood-oxygen levels climbed higher and stayed at the higher level, quite stable. Peter played for half an hour or so and then left. For the whole time he played the monitor alarm did not go off and the baby slept. Ten minutes later his oxygen levels were all over the place again, the alarms were ringing. The nurse was convinced it was the music that had soothed and stabilised him.

On separate occasions when Peter was at the hospital he sought out Nathaniel to play for him, gradually building a relationship with both Nathaniel and his mother.

During Nathaniel's lengthy stay in the nursery Peter went there often to play for him, saying as he entered the nursery, 'Where's my little mate?'

The nurses loved the attention he gave Nathaniel and photographed them together, a photograph that he treasures.

Respecting Geraldine's need for privacy and for her own methods of coping in the early few days, if she was present in the nursery when he went there Peter would play a little away from them; if she was not he would sit close beside Nathaniel's incubator to play for him. Bit by bit Geraldine became accustomed to Peter and they formed a friendship.

It was now approaching Christmas and to create a sense of seasonal normality Peter included in his playing 'Silent Night' or other carols for the babies. Geraldine would sometimes sing softly to the music. She had a lovely voice and told Peter she sang in a choir.

Over the days and weeks, she sang often to Nathaniel as Peter played. Later, Geraldine told me that she had noticed Nathaniel's reaction to Peter's music. She said 'his pulse would slow and so would his breathing. His blood oxygen would go up and the monitor alarms would stop ringing. He just calmed right down'. She thought there was something about Peter. 'The nurses were so busy, we were so worked up, but Peter was calm; there was something about that calmness that made a difference to all of us.'

Geraldine told me a story about a night when Nathaniel was deteriorating and the nurses thought they would need to call them in. Peter was there, he played, Nathaniel stabilised and the nurses ended up not having to call them. The nurses told Geraldine and Pat that they were sure it was Peter and the music that had helped him to improve.

Geraldine's words to me were: 'Peter got him through a few tricky times.'

When it was time for Nathaniel to go home at last, Peter gave Geraldine a CD of his music as a farewell gift, hoping it would help them through some of the challenges ahead. 'When he's old enough,' he told her, 'I'm going to teach him to play the harp.'

Nathaniel had such an uncertain future that to Geraldine these words seemed hopeful.

Weeks passed and Peter visited Nathaniel and Geraldine at home to play for them. Geraldine told him that she played the CD often when Nathaniel was distressed. Always, she told him, when she played the CD he would go limp in her arms, completely relax and go to sleep. When Peter started to play that day in their home, he did exactly that.

Many months later Peter contacted Geraldine to ask her permission to use the photograph of himself and Nathaniel on his website. She gave her permission, but in the course of the conversation she told Peter that tests had shown that Nathaniel was deaf. She had known this just before he left hospital but Peter had not known. He was astounded. How could this small boy respond so profoundly to his music if he could not hear? He asked Geraldine if he could speak to the audiologist about how this could happen and Geraldine gave him the number.

When Peter rang the audiologist she told him that Nathaniel had lost what she called 'middle hearing' and that perhaps he could hear just a little in the upper and lower registers.

'You know,' she said, 'maybe because he's deaf he has developed other senses. Perhaps he's picked up the intention you form for him with your music. Perhaps he senses your care for him.'

Nathaniel started school this year. His leukaemia is in remission, and has been for three years. The doctors tell Geraldine and Pat: 'Consider it gone.'

But not all of the children that Peter plays for will recover. These are the saddest stories: little ones just starting out in life who are not going to live it. Children develop terminal illnesses and parents' dreams are shattered. Parents find the music helpful as they face the dark days ahead, living with their stark loss.

Peter was once asked by the Very Special Kids foundation to play for a little girl who was critically ill. On this day a number of children, including the little girl, and their mothers had come together in a lovely old mansion in Geelong. The owner had donated her living room to the foundation for the day as the space for a pillow concert.

I entered the building with my rug and my pillow. I was a stranger but people smiled at me and the owner of the house was expecting me. She introduced me to the Very Special Kids coordinator from our region, but she didn't disturb any other people. I could see that they were mothers with sick children. Most knew each other. They had been on this path for a while. There were half a dozen or so already present and more people were slowly arriving. They all had pillows and rugs. They seemed to know what to expect; maybe Peter had done this for them before.

We moved through a foyer into a large reception room. I looked around. The ceilings were high and made of pressed tin with ornate designs. Highly polished chandeliers hung from the ceiling but the large windows provided adequate light. The carpet was thick and luxurious, not quite extending to the walls, and revealed polished-wood floors underneath. There were numerous plump and inviting chairs, and couches and coffee tables with vases of spring flowers were scattered around the room. Pictures adorned the walls and heavy dusky pink drapes hung at the bay windows. Outside the windows it was evident that the well-kept gardens were the source of the flowers in the room.

Some of the women lay on the carpet, others on couches. Some, including me, had sunk into the large comfy armchairs. Some children cuddled up to their mothers.

Peter positioned himself amongst them and started to play. His instruction was that they enjoy it. He told them that they did not need to acknowledge what he was doing; he wanted no applause or anything that would break the mood he was building.

He played several of his own compositions, including 'The Ferryman'. Sometimes he hummed or sang softly. One of the mothers started to cry, silent tears running down her cheeks. She bent and hid her face in her daughter's hair. A couple of children fell asleep. One came up close to the harp, watching entranced. Another girl who was slightly older and a little remote and distant when we arrived moved closer to her mother, who received her lovingly. The room was hushed.

When it was over, the child who had been closely watching was invited to touch the harp, to pluck the strings. She did so in wonder, running her fingers in a soft arpeggio, her face lit by a delighted smile. Peter had a reverie harp and he showed her how to use it. She found it different to the upright instrument but she liked it. Peter showed her how to hold it the crook of her left arm and play it with her right hand. When she finished, the reverie harp moved around the room as person after person held it and played a little. Some loved it and didn't want to pass it on. One woman put it on the couch and she and her daughter each played one side of it. Peter offered to lend these mothers instruments so that they and their children could play together.

The mood was gentle and loving when Peter left.

This next story was told to me by a pastoral services staff member. I could tell by the emotion in her voice that the images remained powerful for her.

When she knocked on a patient's door there was no response, so she opened the door slightly and poked her head around. Inside a woman was lying on the bed, white faced and silent. Her partner was sitting on a chair near the bed. He too was pale and drawn, and silent. Separate and alone, they were lost in some deep place of immeasurable sadness.

From the handover, the pastoral services worker knew that this couple's baby had been born prematurely, and that the baby had died during the birth. She entered the room, telling them quietly who she was and how sorry she was for the loss they were experiencing. She sat holding the woman's hand, silently praying for them, that they would somehow find some strength to face this tragedy. She had looked at their records and noticed that they had written 'none' alongside the space for religion. This staff member operated from a place of deep faith, but this couple had no spiritual base and she was at a loss for what she could offer and how she could help.

She told them about the hospital therapeutic musician, and how he played to comfort people. She asked them if they would like him to come and play quietly for them. They both accepted immediately and almost desperately.

She returned to the pastoral services centre and asked Peter if he would play for them.

They went to the room together. The partner was not there and the young woman asked them to come back. They did and he was still not there.

'Why don't you just snuggle down in bed and I'll play quietly for you,' Peter suggested.

She pulled the blankets up over her shoulder, turned and cuddled into the pillow. Not long after her partner arrived. At first he sat on the bed and then he lay on it beside her, cradling her in his arms. Within moments they were both sobbing, holding each other as Peter played.

The pastoral services worker remembers that it was as though a barrier had been removed. 'The music somehow freed them to grieve openly and together. It allowed the emotion to break through the tightness that gripped them.' Watching quietly, she found it a very deep and sacred moment.

Peter asked them if they had chosen a name for their little one. The mother said her name was Maya. 'Let me sing a song for Maya,' he said.

He chose a Celtic tune, 'Garten Mother's Lullaby', the words filled with images of otherworldly care for a baby on her journey through a fog into sleep. It spoke of the comfort of dying embers in a fireside, crickets singing and the expression of love from a mother to her child. He played as beautifully and tenderly as he could – heart-connecting music.

Peter has told me he had tears in his eyes for the place he had personally travelled to in singing this song for Maya and her bereft parents. They were quieter now, the tears stopped for a moment, but were still holding each other and listening to the words of the song and Peter's soft voice.

He played it to them again, humming it this time and

repeated the last line: 'I sing my love to you. I sing my love to you.' Then he left the room quietly, closing the door softly behind him.

Later these parents told the pastoral services worker that it was exactly what they needed in that moment. They hadn't known what they needed until it happened and they were so grateful. They said they felt that it helped them move, where before they had been paralysed by their grief. The following day they went home, with plans made for their future together without this longed-for little baby.

'I knew with certainty,' the pastoral services worker told me, 'that these two people would work through their grief process with wholeness at the end.'

She had witnessed Peter going down to the darkest depths with these people; walking with them at this lowest point and then slowly and gradually, with his presence and his music, bringing them up. She said it was awesome in the truest sense.

19

ℬ

Harp Mysteries

Some people told me stories that were about struggle with illness, not necessarily a terminal illness but one that altered their ability to manage their lives. Rosey found help not through vigils, but though Peter's recorded music. In my research I have argued for the benefits of live music because of the prescriptive possibilities – when Peter can see the person and what is going on around them – but Rosey reminded me that recorded music can also be therapeutic.

In the early 1990s Rosey was in an executive position within the public service in Canberra and endured intolerably high stress levels for many years. This created a long history of seriously debilitating illness. Her problems began in 1994 with infection in both kidneys and an allergic reaction to the antibiotics she was prescribed. Her problems escalated and to this day have not abated. She had to give up her job in 2003, having been deemed one hundred percent mentally and physically incapacitated. She was able to access her superannuation pension and that was the end of her active life.

With a constellation of chronic medical conditions, Rosey is in constant pain, does not sleep and is extremely sensitive to noise, lights and crowds; one trip to the mall can send her 'into a crash'. She has been on the medical merry-go-round for years, and has tried all sorts of other modalities without success: naturopathy, meditation, visualisation and much more. She has even tried music therapy

'If I could list all the harpists and harp-therapy music I've tried . . .' she told me. 'But I'm way too tired.'

Rosey found Peter on the *Australian Story* documentary that ran in June 2010.

'The very first time I tried Peter's music was a week later,' she said. 'One night after taking as much medication as I could safely, and desperate to find relief, I downloaded Peter's *Sanctuary* CD at one am and copied it to my iPod. I went to bed with earplugs, set it to replay, and within three songs the pain lifted and my body was able to release the tension. I fell asleep for seven hours, I think, and I'm pretty sure that was the most sleep I'd experienced for months.'

She purchased all of his CDs, but found *The Sanctuary* to be the most helpful.

'I've found the music to be significant in reducing my pain,' she said. 'This music with my medication regime can have me balanced and back in my body within three or four hours of listening to *The Sanctuary* continuously in bed. Before this it would've been days. I have had sixteen years of severe insomnia, where I lived punch-drunk from ever-accumulating high levels of sleep deprivation. *The Sanctuary* was the first music of any kind that broke the insomnia cycle pretty much permanently.'

Rosey told me that she had never listened to Peter's CD casually for the first few hundred times. 'For me it was a top-shelf treatment that I used specifically to help my pain and insomnia. That in itself says buckets about it. His presence and intention, even on recorded music, his use of pregnant silence and simple but beautiful arrangements allowing the harp's resonance to embrace me . . . I could listen to the same pieces and not tire, nor does my mind become absorbed in predicting a piece, which is common when listening to music. For me, his music aligns my physical, emotional, mental and spiritual self. It relieves the sense of jangled and jadedness my central nervous system experiences with medication, chronic pain, and the assault on the soul, the suffering.'

Rosey mentioned that she had collected the work of the Irish poet and philosopher, John O'Donohue, both in print and in audio format.

'He really highlighted for me the suffering aspect I'd overlooked in my journey, of chronic and acute illness. No one talks about how hard it is to just keep living. The effort, the agony to just do simple things that others think nothing of. And the world is so loud, bright, fast and trivial you're left so isolated, there's a point when you're suffering so much the soul cannot bear it any longer. He was a great man and a great soul now lost to this world.

'I put Peter's whole vocation-intention, music, application, soulful silence and his deep engagement with each precious person, and his knowledge of thresholds "up there" with O'Donohue. It was so obvious to me on *Australian Story* that Peter was exceptional and entered everything soul first with no agenda. He's a beautiful resource for everyone to find shelter from the wretchedness life can throw at one, while he offers sanctuary in grace, kindness and beauty, one can be consoled, touched, healed, from their heart and soul outwards.'

When Rosey told Peter in a letter about her progress with his music, she wrote: *It's quite an awesome gig you have going on* :-)

ℬ'

Just how the CDs help some people and not others is an enigma. Still, stories like Rosey's are plentiful. Peter thinks that it is about encounter with mystery and perhaps one needs to be open to such an encounter. Babies are open because they have not learned to be closed. For older people, maybe some of us can unlearn.

Over the years that Peter and I worked on this book and our research together he mentioned Dr Rosemary Selkirk many times. He told me about the support and encouragement she had given him, and in particular her help in the production of the *Ferryman* CD. I knew he had great respect for her and regarded her as a friend. When Rosemary told him about some special encounters she had experienced through his music, Peter suggested I phone her. I was delighted to speak with this woman he spoke of so highly.

Rosemary has always used music and guided relaxation in her therapeutic repertoire. Exactly what she uses depends on the preferences of her client, and she has noted that not everyone likes the harp. However, she has found *The Sanctuary* particularly helpful. She prescribes the use of the CD now as a first defence for clients with severe anxiety, instructing them to play it for fifteen minutes every day for a week and then return to her to begin their therapy.

In Rosemary's experience, patients who present with anxiety are in a constant state of hyper-arousal to the extent that they are overwhelmed by the constant anxious thoughts and are unable to combat them effectively. Likewise they are generally too stressed to be able to concentrate on a verbal-relaxation CD. She uses Peter's CD to give them the experience of calm and relaxation, something, she reminds us, that we all need to reconnect with in our busy lives. Her aim is to reduce their hyper-arousal to the point where she and her client may begin work.

One client Rosemary told me about had bone cancer and was fearful of facing the surgery he was soon to undergo. In order to help him cope with the intense fear, she gave this man a copy of *The Sanctuary* and he played it over and over during the weeks that followed. The man found that he faced the surgery with courage and managed it far better than he had anticipated. He attributes the positive way he dealt with the surgery to Peter's music. It has now become an intrinsic part of his life.

Another client wrote to Rosemary:

A thoughtful friend gave my husband a copy of Peter Roberts' music CD, and this gift of music was both moving and practical through the ups and downs of cancer treatment. Then in the days before my husband's death, Peter Roberts played for him in his room – a very personal and peaceful experience. One of the things I also found comforting was the way the hospital played 'Brahms' Lullaby' each time a baby was born. We could somehow feel connected to the joy of each new life, even as we struggled and grieved.

One of Rosemary's clients wrote a note for this book about her use of Peter's CD:

When Rosemary and I caught up at a mutual friend's birthday back in March 2011, I relayed to her the diagnosis I had had of a pre-leukaemia, for which the only treatment for cure was a bone marrow transplant. Due to my day-to-day wellness, I delayed treatment so as to support my son through year twelve in the way I wanted. Days later Rosemary sent me Peter Roberts' *The Sanctuary*. From then on I listened to it in bed through my iPod, while reading and then going to sleep. I found most times this music completely centred me. I loved it and it became my calming music almost by association. Sometimes my anxiety about my health was so heightened I would have trouble focusing. I clearly remember many times when I would sit on the back step in the sun, enjoying my garden and listening to *The Sanctuary*. Five or ten minutes later I felt in control and had perspective on my life.

Thank you Rosemary, thank you Peter.

PS. I've now had my transplant and am doing well.

In recent days Rosemary had wondered how she could incorporate Peter's live, prescriptively played music within her clients' treatment. She canvassed several clients whom she felt might benefit and who would be open to listening to music played especially for them. For a trial period she had Peter attend her clinic in Melbourne. Between them they decided it best if Peter was introduced to the clients first, and when they felt the person seemed comfortable with his presence, he would begin to play. He would use his music-thanatology principles to determine what to play and how the time that he and the client were together would unfold. At the conclusion he would leave and Rosemary would commence her therapy session.

Each client's individual music session was recorded, and was given to each person as their personal therapeutic-music resource. This was an experiment to see whether individually prescribed music would be more effective than the general CD.

Two comments below from patients involved indicated that initial feelings of disturbance were followed by calm. Then, knowing that music was specific to them they could choose to use it regularly to the point that the pain would reduce over time as the sense of calm was reinforced.

The first comment was from a man suffering generalized anxiety: 'The music made me very reflective and that generally assists in bringing perspective. My mind wandered to things that are (really) important today, bringing out the core of me, if you both weren't here I'd have bawled my eyes out. Then, peace and calm.'

The second came from a woman suffering depression: 'An amazing journey, a range of feelings, one moment the music tapped some deep well of pain then the harp became very healing, at the end there was a sense of calm and connectedness.'

The trial was shortlived due to the complexity of travel between Melbourne and Geelong and issues about time for Peter, but the concept was a successful one and proved to be very beneficial to these particular clients.

The other area where Rosemary's clients have found the CD useful has been for stressed executives. She recommends they play the CD in traffic or on transport whilst travelling home from work instead of talkback, popular music or the news. The idea behind that is that they arrive home to their families in a better frame of mind than they are used to! Without exception the time-poor executives that Rosemary has worked with have appreciated the benefit and the simplicity of this intervention.

Peter receives letters constantly from people who want to tell him how his CD has helped them. He keeps all of them. Some he shared with me were from people who were sick or in pain; some wrote about relatives.

Francis was desperate to get hold of the CD when her partner was so very sick. Knowing that it would not arrive in time if she ordered it from the IMIM or Threshold Music's website, she downloaded it from iTunes. She played it to him all day on what turned out to be his final day. He died when 'Londonderry Air' was playing, a tune he had often whistled and sung in better times. She wrote:

Thank you sincerely for being you, for making this important, deeply healing music. I believe that it changed the whole presence in the room and calmed everyone and also gave them permission to grieve. I will cherish that song forever and I will never forget that he chose that one.

Francis has told everyone she knows about Peter and his music. Many of her friends have purchased copies, including one who is a counsellor, who plays it for the people she works with who suffer from cancer and aids. She writes that Sydney, the capital city of New South Wales in Australia, is 'desperately in need of a Peter clone'.

Margaret also purchased *The Sanctuary*. She takes it to where she works at a hospice. Her experience is that it is helpful to people on their final journey. Margaret writes:

It is very obvious that when I play the CD to patients they calm and they pass very peacefully. It is amazing to see that they go from terminal restlessness to a very calm state and their breathing is far less laboured. I truly believe that it does make a difference and many families have commented how beautiful it is and have asked about the music. One family has requested to have the music at their loved one's funeral as it gave them such peace at the time of their loved one's death.

Terri wrote of her husband's final days:

I want to thank you so much for sending me the CD of your harp music, and to let you know that I played it constantly during my husband's final days. He died on July 28th, and for the final week he was in the palliative-care room at our local hospital. For his final few days he was in a coma, but he could still hear what was going on around him and could weakly communicate his needs and his love. Your soothing, soul-filled music was with him until the end. It helped fill the room with comfort, colour, and compassion. It reminded both of us of his sister, and his connection to home. And it really touched my heart, and added to my sense of care and love as I sat with Rob, and nurtured him.

There are many such letters.

Marie is the executive director of the Dial A lunch (DAL) Gourmet cafe and catering business in Geelong. Peter told me that her daughter had been helped by his music and suggested I contact her. I did. Marie was delighted to tell the story she thinks everyone should hear. We arranged to meet.

Monday at eleven am. I found a car park quite close by and went into the cafe. It smelled delicious and buzzed with activity. Three or four people were working behind the counter, taking orders and sorting change at the cash register. Customers were sitting around tables sipping coffee and eating snacks. A large door behind the counter opened into the kitchen and I could see more people out there. This is a cafe that employs people with an intellectual disability and at least a dozen people dressed in the checked trousers, white aprons and hats of the hospitality industry were hard at work preparing food or washing dishes. I caught the eye of a woman behind the counter and asked for Marie.

She wiped her hands on her apron. 'Oh yes, she said she was expecting someone.' She disappeared into the kitchen to find Marie.

A woman emerged from a back room. Slim, with short red hair and brightly dressed, she was clearly not one of the hospitality staff. She invited me to join her in the office and directed me through the kitchen. One of the staff members brought coffee and we settled in to talk. I noted her smile, her sparkling eyes and her aura of energy and drive.

Marie started by telling me how her meeting with Peter came about. She had a friend who was dying in the McKellar Centre. In fact she died the day after this event. Marie had wanted her friend to know how much she was loved, not just by Marie but also by many people who had known her at the cafe. She had been told that only family were being allowed to visit so Marie wrote a heartfelt letter. Worried that the letter might not arrive in time if she posted it, she decided to hand deliver it. She took it to the desk and asked the staff member there if she would give it to her friend.

'Would you like to see her?' the woman said.

Marie demurred, saying that she had been told only family were allowed

'Why don't we ask her?'

Marie followed the woman down the corridor toward the room. She saw a man walking toward her pushing a harp on a little trolley in front of him.

She stopped and said to him, 'Are you Peter Roberts?' When he replied in the affirmative she said, 'You can't imagine how important you've been to my family. I've always planned to write to you to tell you about it, but things get in the way and I never got to do it. I want you to know how you helped us.'

She told him the story she was about to tell me. 'Meeting you has made my day,' she said. 'In fact you changed our lives.'

Their meeting was brief, but Marie said that Peter was really touched.

'Well, that deserves a hug,' he said, and his hug was warm.

They went their separate ways and Marie continued toward her friend's room.

Peter told me later that on his way to the car park he was suddenly struck by the thought that hers might be an interesting story for our book, so he went back to find her. He asked Marie if she would like to have her story in print and said he would give me her contact number.

Marie believes this was meant to be. Not posting the letter but delivering it by hand, always wanting to write to tell Peter how much he had helped them, and there he was. How much better it had been to tell him in person rather than by email.

We sipped our drinks in the short silence that followed.

'Tell me your story of how Peter has helped you,' I said to Marie.

Marie's daughter was three years old when she contracted measles. With no vaccination available in those days, she developed encephalitis. Desperately sick, she was admitted to the Fairfield Infectious Diseases Hospital, where she stayed for two weeks. The experience was traumatic for everyone: for little Prue, who was taken from her family; for her sisters, Melinda, six, and Natalie, nine months, who were not allowed in to the hospital; and for Marie and her husband Peter who were devastated by the suddenness and severity of their daughter's illness and fearful of what the long-term effects would be, or even if she would have a long term.

There were no facilities for parents to stay at the hospital. Marie says that if it happened now she would simply insist. Back then, she would arrive at the hospital at seven am and stay till four, and her husband would arrive at four and stay till eleven pm. Marie's parents looked after the other two girls.

Eventually Prue recovered enough to return home, but the little girl they had known was so different. She had regressed.

Her speech was limited and there were many other problems. The once happy carefree child now cried most of the time and was frustrated. The treadmill began. Doctors, specialists, health professionals, program after program of anything that was worth a try to help Prue enjoy life. There were exercise programs and brain-stimulation programs. Her father made her a scooter to help her to use her legs that were so stiff. Prue didn't want a bar of any of it.

Prue was given Dilantin for the temporal lobe epilepsy that she had developed. It was a month-long trial and at the end of it Marie returned to the specialist and told him it hadn't made any difference.

The specialist looked at her incredulously. 'It must have, it has to have made some difference.'

Marie repeated that it had made no difference at all.

The specialist could not believe it and told her so.

'I am her mother,' Marie said. 'I'm with her all the time. I know what she's like and it has made no difference to her at all.' It was so frustrating.

The specialist studied her. 'Perhaps you're stressed,' he said, and wrote a prescription for Valium for both her and Prue.

Incredulous, Marie tore up the script in front of him, threw the scraps of paper on the floor and walked out.

Marie and her husband Peter decided they would do the best they could themselves for Prue. This included finding a very supportive paediatrician in Geelong and an equally supportive GP.

Peter taught Prue to ride a bike, taught her to swim. When school began she went to Morongo Girls' School like Melinda. There were just eight in the kindergarten class and she liked it. She stayed there until she was ten, but in reality she didn't learn much. Some remedial work was available but she could neither read nor write. The other girls in the class were so much more advanced. Prue participated in everything, though, and socially it was helpful.

The next question was: Where to now? Was there a school she could go to that would really suit her needs? Marie discovered the Nelson Park Special School and enrolled Prue. Marie didn't know anything about special schools and felt a bit wary, so she got as involved as she could. She joined the mothers' club, joined the school council, and volunteered for anything she could. Prue was happy and she made some friends.

At home, life was often difficult. While her sisters were great, there were times when they didn't understand. One day Prue wanted something and she was kicking the refrigerator and yelling.

'If *we* kicked the fridge we'd get killed!' her older sister Melinda said.

Marie had to sit them down and explain why Prue could do that and they could not. 'She has no way to tell us what she wants,' Marie told them. 'She just has to do it however she can.'

When Marie would sit Melinda and Natalie down for yet another round of explanations, they would say, 'Uh oh, here we go again.'

But the girls supported their sister strongly and were always patient and protective of her. One day Melinda nearly bashed a boy on the school bus when he called Prue a 'retard'. He never did that again. These days the girls still take Prue on holidays and do 'girlie' things with her to make sure she doesn't miss out. She was bridesmaid at both their weddings and thoroughly enjoyed the responsibility.

The worst thing about their home life was the dreadful nightmares that Prue experienced, from when she came home from hospital, for years and years. She would wake in the night with bloodcurdling screams and her mother would run to calm her. This would happen ten or twelve times every night. Marie remembers sitting on Prue's bed with tears streaming down her face thinking that she might as well never go to bed. She might as well just sit there waiting, all night, every night. Prue would be exhausted the next day and so would everyone else.

Somewhere Marie had read about music therapy and then she came across an article about Peter Roberts and his work in music with people who were sick and dying. Maybe, she wondered, if he could reach people in a coma he could reach Prue in the night.

She took herself off to St John of God and bought his CD *The Sanctuary* from the little shop there. She put it in the machine and pressed repeat so the quiet music would play all night as Prue slept. Prue loved it. If anything happened to stop the music in the night she would call for her mother to start it up again. After six months, the nightmares had reduced to around four or five a night. After twelve months, to four or five a month. After eighteen months she rarely had nightmares at all. Now they are few and far between. Sometimes she even giggles in her sleep.

And now she is alert in the daytime. The whole family exhaustion is over. She is calmer in her everyday life. Nothing else changed in her care, the only thing that Marie can attribute this remarkable change to is the CD. She credits Peter's music with completely turning their lives around. Giving their lives back to them, in fact. Prue is now in her early forties. They had more than thirty years of constant nightmares. They have gone.

Prue's story reminded me of the nurses in the Special Care Nursery who described Peter's presence and his music as 'wrapping them in a soothing blanket of warmth'. When their day was chaotic and stressful he would appear, and after he had played for a time the tension would ease and they would feel in control again. There are medical explanations for this: connecting the autonomic nervous system with the eardrum and body organs such as the heart and lungs.

Perhaps we do not always need medical explanations. Perhaps it is sufficient to think that tenderness and love provided the means to cut through Prue's fear. Music is powerful.

The little reverie harp weaves a similar magic.

Merlene tells a little story about her use of the reverie harp she bought from Peter. She wanted to play for her sister, who has cancer, but she also feels a more general calling to work in music with people who are sick. At first she wanted to learn to play it as one would a guitar, and she was a little disappointed that she could not produce the sounds she was after. Through email conversations, Peter encouraged her to read the booklet and watch the DVD and not to think of the instrument as being anything like a guitar. It is not meant for playing songs, he told her. It is just meant to create a gentle, beautiful harmonic sound.

Merlene was tentative at first, but she persevered. Then she went to visit a friend with Parkinson's disease in a nursing home. Like Merlene, her friend was a midwife but was no longer able to work, and could not care for herself any more.

Merlene wrote to Peter to tell him about this encounter:

You may know that as people with Parkinson's deteriorate they become more emotional and irrational. Often when I visit her she is like that. Today was no exception. She was angry and stroppy. I said, 'Julie, I have something to show you.' She took no notice and began demanding things. After a while I undid the bag and lifted out the harp. I ran my finger along all the strings and she just stopped. I could see her face changing colour then the tears came to her eyes. I laid the harp on her tummy and she gently touched some of the strings. She closed her eyes momentarily and the tears fell. I asked her, 'Are the sounds of the harp touching your heart?' She nodded. She gestured for me to play the harp. I told her I had only just received it and did not know how to play it yet but I would try.

I relaxed and let inspiration guide me. I prayed that the notes would be soothing to her soul. I played for a quarter of an hour and then the nurse came in. She said, 'That is beautiful, I can hear it outside in the corridor.' She came closer and repeated how beautiful it sounded, then she hung about in the room looking for things to do so that she could listen longer. When she had to go she kept repeating how beautiful it sounded and even then she stayed about in the corridor doing things close by so that she could still hear. I kept playing and noticed that Julie had relaxed and was quite mesmerised by the music. Each time I paused she opened her eyes. She never said anything, being quite overcome by the experience. She was calm and peaceful. I played for another half hour and stopped. She looked at the harp and said, 'There is a tree on the harp.' I asked her what the tree meant to her. She said, 'Two hundred years ago an acorn fell to the ground and grew – it grew into a big tree so that you could bring me a harp to listen to and heal my troubled soul.' I played her one more 'song' and I left floating on air. I just had to write and let you know what a blessing it is to have an instrument to heal people. Thank you. For this purpose I bought it. For this purpose I dedicate this harp and my services.

Peter has received many similar letters about the reverie harp. One came from Thelma, whose daughter bought a reverie harp to give to her father for his birthday. At the age of seventy-five, he has had hours of pleasure from the harp. Thelma said she has never known her husband to take to music as he has with the harp.

Sarah plays it in the palliative-care unit where she works and sometimes her patients play it. It has become instantly popular 'singing its sweet way into many hearts'. She has also taken it to funerals, where it is appreciated.

Jemma bought the harp for her own enjoyment. She took it to the botanical gardens and played to the butterflies and the trees. She took it to the sea. She loves its peaceful soothing effect. She has introduced it to her meditation group and the people there said it felt as though they had been meditating for hours instead of minutes.

Nancy is unwell and she has put the reverie harp in her therapy room. She writes: 'It creates such a peaceful, still sacred space, that magical space where there is only stillness.'

Mary, who is a music-thanatologist in the United States, works for a local hospice that had recently purchased a reverie harp. She wrote to Peter to tell him that she had conducted a volunteer-training session at the hospice. She told the volunteers about music-thanatology and also showed them the reverie harp, demonstrating it and telling them about how it could be used. The harp was to be available for them to use in their work if they wished. Mary wrote to Peter: 'They were totally enamoured, couldn't put it down. Thanks for giving birth to such a wonderful notion. It really is a miracle.'

Endorsement like that from someone from Peter's own community of music-thanatologists, who already know the power of the work, is fine praise indeed.

The reverie harp has proven so popular that the Institute of Music in Medicine has created a small harp library, with instruments to be loaned out to individuals who may not be able to afford one, or to institutions that may want to trial one. They come with a smart brass plaque identifying the institute as the owner. We tell people that we want them to be well used. The policy of The Institute of Music in Medicine is that we lend the instrument for a month and then we check to see how it is going. If it is being used and is proving helpful, we are prepared to lend it indefinitely. If it is not being used we retrieve it and offer it somewhere else.

One concern the nurses in the children's ward had was related to the robustness of the instrument and if it could be damaged. Peter has told them that it can withstand being dropped, it can be wiped with disinfecting agents, and if strings break they will be replaced. A few dints and scratches here and there are not a concern to the institute as long as the children and their carers are able to find pleasure and comfort from it.

The children's ward at the Geelong Hospital was one of the first reverie-harp recipients, the palliative-care centre at McKellar the other. We realise that busy nurses may not have time to play an instrument with a child and in the presentation that he did for staff at the hospital, Peter suggested that perhaps some of the volunteer staff might be given the responsibility of taking care of the harp, keeping it fine-tuned and clean. The little reverie harp could be an exciting new tool for the volunteer staff to use to interact with the children. It will be interesting to see how it is used and to hear the outcomes.

Recently Peter conducted a workshop for a group of volunteers from country Victoria. A reverie harp had been purchased for their hospice but they wanted to learn more and to learn how to use the instrument with confidence firsthand from Peter. The workshop was a resounding success and that morning several of these people purchased harps for their own use and to share with their clients. Now The Institute of Music in Medicine is sponsoring a series of these workshops to assist other medical facilities and groups to learn the simple skills required to play them.

20

_ℛ_

Mates and the Missoula Connection

Ted Wilson's daughters, Michelle and Christine, met with me over coffee to tell me about their father. Ted was a policeman for thirty-five years. He started up the police bicycle squad in Geelong and VicRoads named a cycling track after him. He was a strong and fit man, so when he was diagnosed with a heart condition at the age of forty-eight it was a surprise. Ted underwent bypass surgery to graft blood vessels into his heart muscle and he returned to his busy and strenuous life quite quickly.

Then Ted was diagnosed with bowel cancer. It was a shock, but his doctors said that it was contained and could be removed. There would be 'no need for chemo or anything'. They expected to do a simple resection and that would be that. Except it wasn't.

When Ted woke from surgery it was told that his cancer was extensive and had already invaded his liver. His condition was terminal. His surgeon even told him he did not think he would see Christmas. This diagnosis came in 2008. Ted died in 2010.

Throughout his illness, Ted remained cheerful. He continued to cycle and to attend cycling conferences in the States. He did not speak much about the cancer nor about his prognosis. To everyone around him he was the same strong man he had always been, and people took comfort in that, believing that if anyone could beat this disease, Ted could.

During one of his hospitalisations, and there were quite a few, Ted heard music playing near his room. A nurse told him about Peter. She called him the hospital's 'therapeutic musician', reflective of the fact that he played everywhere rather than just in palliative care.

Ted asked the nurse if Peter would play for him and she said she would ask.

Ted was a likeable man. He mixed easily with people and they generally found him quite charismatic. Christine and Michelle said that whenever people were looking for the nurses in the ward, they would find them in Ted's room. Peter liked him too, immediately. Most times that Ted was admitted to the hospital Peter would see him on the admission list and would visit him. Often when his daughters arrived they would find Peter and Ted talking together. Peter did play, but they seldom saw that; mostly they found them chatting.

Peter has said that this was a man he would have liked to call a friend. He remembers with emotion Ted's passing, and his memory is of having lost a mate.

Michelle remembers her father as a strong man, at least on the exterior. That was what made it so hard for them when it became obvious that he was dying, this man whom they thought could survive anything. She said that her father's reaction to Peter's music was immediate and powerful. Every time he spoke of Peter or of the harp music he would become emotional. Ted spoke to her sometimes about having cancer, and about his struggle with the thought of dying. Michelle was a nurse and she supposed that her father thought she was familiar with death and cancer and he could have such a conversation with her. Ted bought a copy of Peter's CD *The Sanctuary*, and played it often at home. His daughters do not remember their father as ever having been interested in music, but this music captivated him completely.

One day when Peter was visiting Ted, he noticed there was a stuffed toy, a raccoon, on the bed. 'What's the story behind this?' he asked Ted.

'I have lots of grandkids who come in to visit,' Ted said, 'so I bring it in for them to play with. I bought it on one of my trips to America, in a place called Missoula.'

Peter was stunned. 'Missoula! I know it well.' And he proceeded to tell Ted all about his own experience of Missoula.

'No one knows about Missoula here in Australia,' he told Ted. 'I've never met anyone who has been there or who knows it.'

They could then share stories of the bike trails in Missoula, the shops where Ted bought his boots, people they knew in common. It cemented an already growing friendship. Ted bought a reverie harp from Peter. He could never play it well, and not being able to make music on it frustrated him sometimes, but often the girls would arrive and he would be lying or sitting with it on his chest, and he would move his fingers over the strings from time to time.

Ted's family nursed him at home at the end and he died there peacefully. Peter's last visit was around a week before he died. Several family members were there; some stayed for the music, some left. Ted did not really wake. A child was making happy sounds and the atmosphere was peaceful.

Michelle thought that the music helped people to be still and peaceful around her father. 'Often people want to be doing something, or talking, filling the quiet, but the music would create silence and stillness where people could just be there, feeling comfortable with the silence.'

Christine thinks that the harp music helped Ted with the struggle of dying. 'That's why he wanted the harp music all the time. He was weak, too weak to talk really, but he connected to the music. It took him to some tranquil place.' Ted had not spoken of dying to Christine as he had with Michelle, but she knew he was dying and toward the end she said to him that if he needed to go he could go.

One day Christine felt compelled to visit. He was not able to talk, but he mumbled, 'I love you, mate.'

She put her head on the pillow beside him, and he asked what she was doing. 'I'm giving you a hug, Dad.'

'Why are you crying?' he said. Then he seemed to wake out of this deep drowsy state, looked up, put his hands up and said, 'Heaven, I'm ready, take me.'

After which he returned to his deep drowsy state. He died the next day. He was never a religious man, but his daughters thought that he had found a deep spirituality.

Michelle looks back at emails she wrote to overseas friends after Ted died. They read: 'He passed away, speaking to the end . . . Couldn't have asked for a better way for him to die, a better death . . . Couldn't have done anything more for him . . . He died peacefully . . . It was a beautiful experience.'

The emails sum up what Ted's daughters told me in their story about him. They were tearful during the telling, but smiling in their love for him and the pleasure of the memory of their dad and the way he died.

Even now, Christine plays Peter's CD and her little boy laughs delightedly, 'This is Pa's music,' he says. She loves that they have this shared memory of something that was so important and that influenced the way Ted died.

More than a year after I spoke to Michelle and Christine, I met Maree, Ted's partner. Maree had not seen the advertisement I placed in the local paper but she had maintained a friendship with Peter and Jeanette and so learned of the book. Peter invited her to speak with me about her experience of Ted's illness and his involvement with Peter and music-thanatology.

We met at Costa's, the cafe at St John of God, on a Friday afternoon. I selected a table at the back for privacy, which turned out to be a wise decision since her experience of Ted's death is still raw for her. We got a coffee and settled in to talk.

Like Ted, Maree had been in the police force and in the bicycle unit. She and Ted were colleagues for fifteen years. She described Ted as a visionary and an entrepreneur, dreaming up the ideas for the bike unit, which she, being more pragmatic, would help bring to life. As work colleagues it seemed they were perfectly matched. It was not until the later years that their working relationship deepened into a personal one and they became life partners. Maree described Ted as a charismatic man, personable and quirky. He got on well with anyone and loved to chat. There was genuineness about him and a wonderful, wicked sense of humour.

When Ted was diagnosed in 2008 he decided to have surgery and then chemotherapy. He understood that the illness he had been diagnosed with was terminal, but he was hopeful of some quality time ahead. His oncologist Adam Broad, who Maree still speaks of with respect and gratitude for how well he cared for Ted, was able to offer a number of options but he was always honest about the ultimate outcome of Ted's illness.

Ted met Peter while he was in hospital in the early days of his illness. He knew about 'Brahms' Lullaby' playing when a baby was born, and he was lying in bed and heard the music.

Ah, he thought, a new little one. Then he heard it again. Twins? he thought. But then he heard it again and again. Confused, he got out of bed and walked down the corridor to ask the nurse what the music was, and she told him. He walked to the sunroom and there was Peter playing for a group of patients. He stayed to listen and then asked Peter if he would play for him occasionally. He played for him that day.

Treatment was going well enough for Ted to plan to travel to a bicycle conference in September 2008 in the USA. He really wanted to go because his close friend who directed that conference was about to retire and he thought it would be his last opportunity to catch up with his overseas friends.

The conference was in Seattle and Ted did get there. After the conference he travelled to catch up with another close friend, this time in Missoula, Montana. We know the story of the stuffed toy that he bought there, and how that linked him to Peter in friendship.

Maree first learned of Peter when visiting Ted in hospital.

'I had a visit from this man today,' he said. 'His name is Peter Roberts.' He told her about the sunroom encounter and the stuffed racoon story.

Over the time Ted was in hospital Peter brought him magazines and clippings that he had about Missoula and they spent time reliving pleasant memories.

One of the few times Maree actually heard Peter play was in the oncology day-stay unit where Ted would go for chemotherapy. She is still reflective about the time he played for Ted there. There were a number of patients in for treatment that day.

Peter came in with his harp and sat down smiling at people around the room. He started to play a piece of music, then stopped and said, 'No, that's no good,' and moved to something else.

Maree felt he was trying to work out what to play, feeling his way, trying to work out what felt right. She had the sense that he was searching for the right music for Ted and that everyone else in the room was kind of peripheral. She said it is a brief but somehow significant memory, Peter working hard to find something to help them.

Maree and Ted had many deep conversations about their lives together, his approaching death and his struggle with leaving. In one conversation she asked him if he believed in an afterlife. He paused to think and then said, 'Yes, I do.'

Thinking about life after death gave him a sense of meaning and some comfort. Ted was not a religious man, but Maree said he was a spiritual person. Maree is Catholic and her faith helps her. She too believes in an afterlife and it gives her comfort believing that she and Ted will meet again. She believes that death doesn't end a relationship. It just changes it.

When Ted bought the reverie harp from Peter, they both went to Peter's home to collect it when it was ready. They met Jeanette, who they both warmed to immediately. The connection continues and last year Jeanette took one of the community courses that Maree runs in getting woman back onto bikes. Theirs is an easy friendship that Maree treasures. Ted's purchase of the reverie harp, she thinks, was because it was something that he could leave his grandchildren. He was captivated by Peter's description of how he uses it with children.

Toward the end, the house was set up so that family could care for Ted. A palliative bed was brought in. His family was there constantly, helping care for him. Peter offered to come to their home in Ted's last days. Maree said he didn't play for a long time, but it was beautiful. Ted was not very responsive but he knew Peter was there. She felt it was special that Peter took the time to come and offer them comfort and peace in those last days.

Ted died at home on 1 July 2010 surrounded by loved ones. Maree misses him and grieves for him. She treasures the time with Ted, and especially the four years they lived together. She still plays Peter's *Sanctuary* CD and still derives comfort from it.

21

♌'

Birthdays, Bellies and Blue Suede Shoes

In palliative care, Peter's day starts with a private ritual that he devised. He centres himself, and then washes his face, hands and eyes, committing his senses to a higher purpose. He prepares to move from one way of being to another. Then he goes into someone, radar wide open, acutely aware of everything in the room, any sounds, anything that happens.

'There's a serious preparation for this work and my preparation heightens my intent,' he says. He quotes Yehudi Menuhin, who said, 'To play one needs an eye not only on music but on a distant star.'

He is ready. He walks into a room, pushing the harp on its little trolley ahead of him.

There are many stories in palliative care: in every room, on any day. Some are humorous, some are about fleeting encounters, some are thought provoking and some (most) are poignant. A palliative-care volunteer at the McKellar palliative-care unit, a woman with a wealth of insight, compassion and humour, told me this story.

She went into the room of a man who was terminally ill and found him sitting in a chair weeping.

'What's going on in here then?' she asked him.

'It's my wife's birthday today,' he said through his tears.

'Ah,' the volunteer said, 'and you haven't got anything to give her.'

He shook his head sadly.

'Well, I can fix that.'

From somewhere, who knows where, she located flowers and brought them to him. He put them on the bed gratefully. Then she found Peter and told him about this man and his wife's birthday.

'Perhaps when she comes you can play "Happy Birthday" to her,' she said.

Peter agreed. They went to the room, found that the man's wife had not yet arrived and put the plan to him and he agreed. And smiled.

When the man's wife arrived both Peter and the volunteer were in the room. Peter played for her and when he finished they were all laughing. He started to play other songs and they sang along. There was not much that was vigil-like going on there now, although this man was certainly dying.

Peter asked the woman whether there was something in particular she would like him to play, and she told him about her father, who was a country preacher. He played some songs he thought might resonate: 'Abide With Me', 'Amazing Grace' and others.

At one point the volunteer said to the couple, 'I guess if I wasn't here you two would be holding hands.'

'Oh yes,' the woman responded, 'he likes to hold my hand all the time, even when we're in bed.'

So she moved the furniture around to make it easier for her to sit closer to her husband. They held hands.

Peter then played the song called 'Perhaps Love' written by John Denver. It is a song about the strength of love and how the memory of love can sustain through dark times. Denver wrote it about his wife from whom he was separated and he was telling her that his memories of love would forever be about her. Peter sensed that this song would be meaningful for them and in the quiet that followed the volunteer winked at Peter and they quietly left the room.

Peter spoke with an occupational therapist who was attending this man, who added to this story. She said that the woman told her that she really enjoyed her birthday, which she hadn't done in years. Her father had died on her birthday many years before. Every birthday since then all she ever felt was sadness and her family had never understood why her birthday was never joyful for her.

'I've loved this birthday,' she told the therapist, 'and I'll enjoy all my birthdays from now on.' She said this despite the fact that she was soon to lose her husband. She felt this memory would sustain her.

This might seem a story about sensitivity and compassion rather than about music-thanatology, but it is also about intuiting, in the moment, what is needed, which is intrinsic to music-thanatology. In this case it was about intuiting what would help this couple in their last days together.

Occasionally Peter connects with someone he plays for in a different way, when something clicks between them that is more than the vigil encounter, as it did with Ted. These encounters are relatively rare, maybe two or three in all the years he has been doing this work.

Peter played for Kathryn's father Robert in the palliative-care unit. Kathryn told me about her father and how he met Peter.

'I know at first Dad was a little apprehensive,' she said. 'He would hear the harp music in the distance and laugh and say, "Oh God, the angels are coming." But after Peter came into Dad's room and played for him he absolutely loved it. He was fascinated with its therapeutic benefits. He said it made him feel light and calm.'

Kathryn remembered the day when the whole family was there. 'We were at the palliative-care unit most of the time and Dad liked that Peter involved us as a family, letting his four year old grandson Jack have a little play of the harp, and myself as well. The funny thing is, the first day Dad went to McKellar Centre was on a Monday. I spent all day there, so I studied everything in his room. When I came home I sat on the couch and flicked the TV onto *Australian Story*. I rarely watch this. It was about Peter Roberts. I kept saying to my husband, "That's the same sort of room Dad's in, it's even got the same mark on the wall." Later in the show they showed the room number and it was Dad's exact room! It was a very mixed reaction for me, going from how bizarre to see that show on that day, to the harsh reality of what was actually going to happen in that room.'

And then she met Peter and he played for her dad.

'What Peter does is such a beautiful thing. We certainly benefited and looked forward to his visits to the palliative-care unit. He helped us as a family to smile when we didn't really feel like it. If we weren't there when Peter came in then Dad had much joy in telling us "Guess who I had all to myself today?" with a smug grin.'

When I returned this story to Kathryn for checking, she

wanted to add this little message to Peter: 'Peter, you are a beautiful, caring and giving man. You not only help the patients in palliative care; you also help the families to find calmness and strength.'

Janice told me the story of her sister-in-law, Sandra. It is humorous: more laughter amid tears.

Sandra was in the palliative-care unit. Janice wove a wonderful image of this woman who was very close to the end of her days, but who was wearing a purple nightgown and lying in a bed with purple sheets and pillowcases. Her quilt was purple with silver stars, and Janice's description was of a vibrant, fun-loving woman. Sandra's friends and relatives had brought meaningful things in to decorate her room. Nothing in there resembled a hospital room. Janice showed me a photograph of Sandra nestled in purple and I could see her smiling face and her alert gaze. People surrounded her. In fact, right to the end her room was always full of people who loved her dearly.

Sandra had talked about dying. She was ready. All of these people came to support her last days and to keep vigil with her to the end. This was not morbid, but it was sad. Janice said that her sister-in-law was always smiling, right to the end. She had so much courage.

Sandra's brother Mark had come to visit on this particular day, and he heard harp music playing somewhere in the building as he entered. He asked a staff member what it was and she explained Peter's role in the palliative-care unit. Mark asked if Peter could play for Sandra, and Peter said he certainly would but he would be a little while. He had a few others that he had promised to visit first.

One of the people Peter had promised to play for was an elderly woman. In her room were a couple of other older people and a younger couple. He started to play. One of the women began to hum, and Peter pricked up his ears, liking her involvement.

'You know Elvis is here,' she said.

Peter wondered what on earth she meant.

'Do you know any Elvis music?' the woman asked.

Peter said he knew a few pieces, and started to play 'Love Me Tender' gently and soothingly.

The young man in the room joined in. He had a deep rich voice and sounded just like Elvis. Turned out he was an Elvis impersonator and worked the cruise ships. They had a fine time, Peter playing as 'Elvis' sang.

Eventually, Peter arrived in Sandra's room. He noted the purple everywhere and was surprised that the room was full of people, chatting and passing savoury snacks. It was like a party. This would be a different kind of a vigil, he realised. Maybe more like party entertainment, not his usual offering. He greeted people, then found a chair and started to play.

'Well, that was nice,' Sandra said.

Peter picked up that it was not her thing. He asked what she would like him to play for her and she told him that she was an Elvis fan and would love to hear something of his.

'Well,' said Peter, 'I can do better than that.'

And he left their room, returning with the Elvis impersonator, who agreed to sing for Sandra.

Peter played 'Love Me Tender' again and the man sang along. When he got to the part, 'Oh my darling, I love you . . .' he was on one knee, his hand outstretched to Sandra. When he finished he left the room with a flourish, saying, 'Elvis has left the building.'

Everybody laughed.

Then Peter played 'Love Me Tender' again, slowly and

tenderly, and everyone held hands in a half-circle around the bed and swayed to the slow music as he sang to her. Sandra loved it. Janice said that the little Elvis concert was such a memorable moment; everyone felt very loving and later her friends often talked about it. Peter learned later that the Elvis impersonator returned to Sandra again on another occasion and sang to her. Janice said he sang 'Blue Suede Shoes', another of Sandra's favourites.

Because Peter only plays at Barwon Health one day per week, and at St John of God two days per week, some people's experience of him and his music are only fleeting. Even those are often quite powerful encounters. The following stories illustrate this.

Cliff responded to an advertisement that I placed in the local paper inviting people who had a story to tell about Peter Roberts and his music for this book. When I met him he told me how he met Peter while he was visiting a man who had been a close friend and mentor.

'I was making a cuppa at the Grace McKellar Centre in December 2006. I was visiting a man called Tom, who was dying from throat cancer. Tom was not only my closest friend; he had also been my mentor for my problems with alcohol addiction. Tom had helped me stay sober for around eighteen months at the time of his passing. I'm still sober today. I believe I would have died or gone insane if not for Tom's influence in my life.

'Back to the day I met Peter. I'd been making a cuppa when Peter walked into the room and proceeded to make himself one. He said hello and asked me if I was there to visit a friend or relative. Although I didn't really feel like talking, because I was choked up about Tom, I told him why I was there. I'd never met Peter before, but I could see in his eyes that he seemed to really care and it felt kind of soothing to talk with him.

'I asked him if he was also visiting a friend or relative and he said no, he told me that he plays music on a harp for people who are seriously ill. He asked if he could get his instrument and play for Tom. To be honest I thought this was a bit odd and I asked him how much he charged. When he told me it was free, I told him that I would check with Tom's wife Marg if it would be okay. She said yes and so Peter brought his instrument to Tom's room. He began to play this huge harp and it sounded like something you would hear in an old movie when an angel appeared. Tom's eyes were closed and I didn't know if he would hear it. He had been slipping in and out of consciousness for the past two days.

'Suddenly Tom opened his eyes and said, "Its a harp!" He had a huge smile on his face. Then he drifted back to sleep still smiling. Peter continued to play for about twenty minutes, and then he quietly packed the instrument away. Marg and I whispered, "Thank you." He acknowledged us with a smile, then left.

'Tom passed away the next morning around ten am. The words, "Its a harp!" and the huge smile on Tom's face are my final memory of him. I made some enquiries about Peter's role at the hospital and I was amazed when staff told me that Peter wasn't told which patients are about to die. I now believe that Peter is somehow guided to those that need him to help them let go of the fear of death. I have wondered if he is some kind of angel or if he is guided somehow spiritually.'

Cliff reflected for a moment and then said, 'If I had known Peter's purpose in Tom's life, then I may not have allowed him to play that day, because I wasn't ready to lose Tom. I now believe that Peter's meeting with me happened exactly as it was meant to, at precisely the right time. I bumped into Peter about twelve months ago at a cafe in Highton and I thanked him again for his music that day at the hospital. He seemed to remember me, and we spoke for a little while about his amazing gift. But of course Peter is too humble to accept any real praise for his work. I will be forever grateful for his role in bringing peace and ease to Tom's final hours.'

Kevin also responded to my advertisement. He wanted to tell me about his friend Jill.

Jill was diagnosed with melanoma thirty-five years before she finally succumbed to it. It was treated surgically and she recovered well. At the age of sixty, she found a lump in her groin, probably a secondary from that original cancer. Kevin describes Jill as flamboyant and extroverted, a joyful woman who lived an enormous life. Her life revolved around her friends, but not in a needy way; she was a most self-content person.

Jill had been an actor. She did a one-woman show at the Pram Factory to fabulous reviews. She had also been a nurse and an occupational therapist. She worked in the United States as an occupational therapist for five or six years, then in Mt Isa and in aboriginal communities in Central Australia and in Port Lincoln. None of it was easy work because she was a formidable woman, a force to be reckoned with when she didn't think that things were as they should be. She was sensitive and didn't really court conflict, but she was always controversial and did speak out, often with adverse consequences to herself. People loved her and called her 'Aunty Jill of the outback'.

When Jill was diagnosed with secondary cancer, she was in Port Lincoln. She decided to move closer to Kevin and his wife for company so that, in the end, they could help her.

In the beginning, not much changed about the way she lived, She had a passion for music and people, and loved good food. In fact she would spend anything on good food and restaurants. She lived what could only be called a 'high life'.

Jill was in severe pain as the cancer progressed. The health professionals caring for her kept revising plans for pain control, trying to stay on top on it. Toward the end the pain was so severe and the medication so strong she would be as Kevin described 'off her tree'. Kevin and his wife and others took turns to stay with Jill overnight to keep her safe.

The day before Jill was admitted to Grace McKellar, at a restaurant called Oakdene, Jill had a fabulous meal of pork belly. As she lay in agony at Grace McKellar the following day, she half opened her eyes, grinned at Kevin and his wife and said, 'The pork belly done me in.'

The tumour had perforated her bowel; she had peritonitis and was in agony. Her sister in Tasmania was notified, and in order to get an emergency flight over she asked for a letter from the doctor to be faxed to her.

That is how Kevin met Peter. He thought Peter was a volunteer and asked to be directed to a fax machine. Peter took him to one and stayed to help him. While it was going through, Kevin told Peter about Jill, and Peter told Kevin about his work. They arranged that Peter would play for her.

It happened to be on the Friday afternoon before the Australian rules football grand final. Jill was a very keen supporter of the Collingwood team. They were to play St Kilda in the final. Just for a joke, Kevin asked Peter to play 'When the Saints Go Marching In', the theme song of the St Kilda Football Club. Jill was not conscious, but later she said she was aware and recalled hearing it, and laughed heartily.

Peter played many other tunes, some of his own compositions, some music Kevin and others told him she would love. Kevin mentions 'Mull of Kintyre' as a lovely lyrical tune that Jill particularly liked. Only Kevin and his wife were with Jill when Peter played for her and this added to the intimacy and poignancy for them.

Kevin was struck by the amazing innovation of offering harp music at a time like this and wished Jill's numerous friends could have been present. He wished Peter could have stayed all night, for as long as it took. Unfortunately, Peter was not able to return before Jill's death on the Sunday morning.

Kevin had worried that Peter's music might be cloying and embarrassing; they didn't want to be maudlin around Jill. Peter seemed to know that, and he was sensitive and genuine, sombre but certainly not maudlin. Kevin thought that Peter pitched the selections of music perfectly. He simply focused on Jill and played for her. Kevin was so awed by the experience at the McKellar palliative-care unit – the staff, the music-thanatology, the focus of everyone on Jill and making her last days as comfortable and pain free as possible – that he even wrote to the minister for health in Canberra to let him know about the experience.

Only one vigil was held for Rose in the nursing home, although he had played for her once in the hospital. Peter's intuition was that she had found it helpful and so he rang the nursing home to ask if she would like him to come.

The nurse who took the call went to check with the family, she returned and said, 'Yes, they think that would be great.'

We drove the hour or so to the nursing home. When we arrived, it was evident she was very close to death. Her family was around her, one by her bedside, others around the room a little further back. The daughter by the bed smiled a quiet welcome as we entered. She told us that her mother had smiled and her face lit up when she was asked if she would like Peter to come and play.

As Peter started to play she seemed asleep, but after a moment she opened her eyes and smiled at him and slowly withdrew her arm from under the covers and held her hand out to him. He took her hand and sat quietly for a moment. She smiled and closed her eyes and drifted off again, so Peter resumed playing.

When he finished, she roused enough to look at her daughter and say, very weakly, 'Did you like it?'

'It was wonderful,' her daughter responded. 'Now I understand what you were saying.'

It seems that her mother had tried to tell her family about something that had happened to her in the hospital. She could not find the words to describe it and so she stopped trying, except to say that it had been profound and important. Her daughter told us that she believes it was Peter's playing that she was trying to describe to them. They were grateful that they had been present to witness this gift to their mother.

Paul sent Peter a letter of thanks for his music after his wife died at St John of God. This is from his letter:

It was the week sandwiched between the drawn grand final and the replay the following weekend: the last week in September of 2010. The hospital felt like an island as the Cycling Championships had blocked most streets. My darling wife was moved to the room adjacent to the nurses' station, level 1 in St John of God in Geelong.

We had been together for thirty-eight years. Our two beautiful children, Billy and Eve, and Jill's mum and sister from Perth were there. We were not prepared fully for her passing as we thought there would be at least one more Christmas . . . maybe two.

I had noticed you in one of the corridors and was mesmerised by the beautiful simplicity of what you were doing. The notes from heaven were gently moving through the wards. It seemed like each note floated directly to the heart for its healing purpose. You took up a position right outside her room and filled our most sacred space with love and healing. The perfume of flowers and your music . . . the world at a standstill . . . all of our senses filled to overflowing. And it is this, so imprinted in each of us there, that will last forever.

Each note gently played for Jill's final moments . . . her beautiful being easing gracefully.

Jill also held deep conviction for the sensitivity and sacred assistance for those most vulnerable, and in stages of fragile unwellness. All of her working life as a professional hairdresser she worked in Hospice & Palliative care settings, Para & Quadriplegic Rehabilitation, Hospital and Home visiting service, and a significant time with a Shire Care Services team where she specialised in assisting people with complex mental health problems. She plunged herself into these roles with passion and a determination to know and fully understand the complex journey of mental health and caregiving. She took on studies and before long was appointed the Carer Consultant for North East Region Mental Health. Her drive and bold operational style in acute care settings endeared her to all who came to know her. She was honoured by senior staff of mental health and all who knew her at her funeral service for the true care giving champion that she was.

So you can see why we are so touched by your request to share our story in your book. We are true believers in the extraordinary and holy repertoire of sacred moment therapies. But it is so much more than that . . . and this is what

I meant about the difficulty of finding words . . . it is that the chosen intervention does actually speak for itself. There is no explanation needed for what it is, or the extraordinary set of effect and outcome that transpires.

I cannot thank you enough. There don't appear to be the words to adequately say what your music did. People will commend you in all quarters for what you are doing, as they should, but it is when you are actually the beneficiary right there at the final sacred space and the direct recipient of your beautiful work. This is the high order testimonial.

Not long after Jill's passing, I found myself putting together some lyrics for a distant song and called it Measure of Care. But the lyrics pay tribute to Jill and the fact that there is no measure. Perhaps the deepest honour that we can bestow on selfless caregiving is to simply acknowledge that there is no boundary, no yardstick, no defined end adorned with clever adjectives . . .

That the Measure of Care has no measure. It just is.

May your beautiful work continue and if there were any occasion or manner in which you might be supported, please let me know.

Thank you from our hearts,

Jill (dec.), Edna, Annette, Billy, Eve and Paul

Marion's father Bruce lived with prostate cancer for eighteen years. He had chemotherapy, improved, then relapsed and developed system failure. He was never in pain, right to the end, and the family was grateful for this. Throughout her life Marion kept a daily diary. She recorded the first time Peter played for her father: it was 14 April 2009. She wrote that her father had enjoyed it but that he had insisted that there be no 'Danny Boy'. He hated it.

Peter asked him what he would like and he said he wanted 'My Redeemer Liveth'. Peter said that he didn't know it but he would make it his business to learn it for him.

Two days later Peter was playing this tune for Bruce when he died. He knew that Bruce was very close to death, so, as Marion said, 'He just dropped by.' He played all of the songs that her father loved, including the one he had requested. Marion thinks that Bruce had been aware that Peter was there before he died, even though he didn't respond.

Peter kept playing, maybe for fifteen minutes, after Bruce had died. Several family members were there, and they talk about that time even now. They have a lingering memory of this as a special time and that Peter and his music had comforted them. Marion said she had dreaded being there when her father died, but she has a loving memory, without sadness, and she was so pleased that she had been there.

There is another small story that I have put together from what several people told me. Peter struggled through tears to tell me his account. Like so many of these stories, it was hard to tell and to write, but it is powerful.

On this particular day Peter walked down the long corridor of the palliative-care unit, pushing his harp ahead of him. The harp was almost as tall as he but he manoeuvred it easily around corners and in between equipment, trolleys and people who were walking purposefully along the corridors. He had just come from a meeting where the pastoral-services team had referred people who might benefit from his work. Staff members greeted him and smiled as he walked by, some commenting on the harp. Peter made this harp himself and he was the only person who played it. He knew every nuance of it. The instrument knew him too, it seemed, responding to his touch, surrendering music so beautiful.

A nurse touched his arm to stop him. She gestured to one of the doors. 'The man in here is really distressed,' she said. 'I don't know if you can do anything, but . . .' She told Peter that nothing she had offered this man had helped. Medicine had reached its limits.

Peter entered the room and his gaze was immediately drawn to the bed. An elderly man was thrashing around. He had yellow parched skin and blotches on his face and neck. He was bald, with just a few white hairs sticking up. The blotches were on his scalp too, like sores. His spindly legs were out of the bedclothes and flailing about. His hands plucked at the sheet. His eyes were shut, his face contorted. He made no sound and did not respond when Peter spoke to him or touched his shoulder. The scene was distressing. The man was close to death and it looked like a dreadful way to die.

A woman in the room, a relative of the man, recognised Peter. She started to greet him, observing social niceties. Peter's focus was on the man and his distress and he found the social observance difficult. He smiled a greeting and then moved to sit closer to the man, right up by his face and leaning in to him. He started to play.

Gradually, some ten minutes into the playing, the thrashing around slowed. Bit by bit the man settled, moved onto his side, curled up in a foetal position facing the harp, close to the edge of the bed. It was as if he was trying to wrap himself around the harp. His agitation had gone. He was still. Peter moved further in, as close as he could to the man, the pillar of the harp touching the bed by his chest. The man had no words to say that he felt comforted, but everything about his response was so powerful it was like a shout. This was like a man dying of thirst in the desert who suddenly finds water.

After a time, Peter stopped playing and quietly left the room.

He had done what he went there to do. It was now peaceful in there. Moments later the nurse found him to say that the man had died. His relatives told her that it happened as soon as the playing stopped. There was no movement, no sound. He just slipped away peacefully.

Music-thanatologists frequently play right through the moment of death and after the person has died they often keep playing to help the relatives with the moment. We have heard that in the intensive-care unit of one hospital in the United States, the intensivist doctor has made music-thanatology the gold standard for removing breathing tubes from people who are not going to survive their illness or injury. That means that when the decision is made to extubate (remove the tube), the music-thanatologists are booked and the procedure does not commence until they are in the room and playing.

The doctor who instigated this wrote that generally when the decision is made to extubate, all staff disappear and the doctor is alone. It is too difficult to witness. But she said that when she introduced music-thanatologists for the procedure, she looked around the room and found that staff had crowded in; they were lined around the walls and peering over shoulders at the door. Suddenly this moment of death had reverence that people wanted to be part of. It changed everything. Would that this could happen in every hospital where relatives and staff members have to make these decisions and witness that moment.

There was a woman dying in the palliative-care unit. She was exhausted, ready to go and tired of the wait. She wanted to be left alone; she did not want to be disturbed. She had a nurse type a notice for her door:

SHH SHH
I AM RESTING
PLEASE DO NOT DISTURB

And handwritten underneath this sign were the words:

PLEASE COME IN PETER ROBERTS

With a little smiley face beside it ☺

Acknowledgements

∂

Helen: My first acknowledgement is to Peter, who invited me to research the amazing work that he does with such humility and love, and who trusted me to do it with sensitivity. Thank you to the many patients and relatives who were part of our studies or who answered my advertisement for stories and who also trusted me to treat their experiences with delicacy and care. Thank you to the executive of the St John of God Hospital and particularly to the director of mission, Trish Boom, who facilitated the studies and my presence in the hospital. Thank you to the various health professionals: pastoral-services practitioners, nurses, doctors and others, including volunteers, who told me of their experiences with music-thanatology and who also assisted with the various studies in both hospitals.

Thank you to my family. My husband Doug who graciously bought himself a new computer so I could monopolise one, and who cheerfully managed without my company for great expanses of time while I wrote. To our daughter Nicole and her family, Justin, Romani and Kashi in England; our sons and their families, David and 'Cint, and Greg, Donna, Zoë and Max; and my brothers and sisters. All have been encouraging and supportive.

Thank you also to Writers Victoria, especially my writing mentor Lee Kofman for the hours spent commenting on and shaping my writing. The members of The Year of Creative Non Fiction Class led by Sian Prior helped me clarify the content and direction of the book. Huge thanks to Dr deSales Turner for her helpful comments on the chapters in section 1.

Finally, and critically, thanks to Michelle Anderson of Michelle Anderson Publishing for her immediate interest in the concept of our book and for her encouragement throughout the writing process, and to Penny Springthorpe for her sensitive and expert editing of the manuscript.

Contact Helen Cox
www.helencox.com.au

Peter: There are so many people to thank in the creation of a book like this but it is an impossible task. There are the ones I have played for who have now left us. There are the young parents of tiny, struggling premi babies . . . and so many others. Our paths crossed only briefly, but you allowed this stranger with his harp into the intimate moments of your life at times of great vulnerability. Thank you for trusting me.

To my dear wife Jeanette, who has shared life with me for the past forty years. I am so grateful for your fond company. It's been quite a journey and I'm blessed to have been travelling it with you.

To our daughters, Katherine and Ellise, who have shared it too, thank you for your sense of fun along the way, your friendship and good hearts. I'm so proud of the caring, open and thoughtful women you have become.

To Joy and Harry and all who have played a part in encouraging me in my music, and to those who have believed in the uncharted course it was taking me on. You are too numerous to mention but know you are dear to me.

Acknowledgements

To Helen Cox, who could see the value in sharing these stories beyond the confines of hospital wards with those who have no experience of this world at all. Thank you for your sensitivity, your strength and your skill in guiding the formation of this book. Thank you also for encouraging me to write my own story and for being my friend and confidant since our first meeting.

To Michelle Anderson of Michelle Anderson Publishing, who believed in the concept we presented to her: I am grateful for your trust in enabling us to bring our story to the public.

To Penny Springthorpe: thank you for your keen observational skills, the tact you showed, and the encouragement you offered during our final editing.

Contact Peter Roberts
www.robertsmusic.net

References

Anam-Aire P. *A Celtic Book of Dying: Watching With the Dying, Travelling With the Dead*. Findhorn Press, Scotland.

Byock I. (1997) *Dying Well: Peace and Possibilities at the End of Life*. Riverhead Books, New York.

Cox H. (2005) 'Relief of suffering at the end of life: Report from an Australian project to implement and evaluate a live harp music-thanatology program.' Report to Deakin University, St John of God Hospital & Kings Australia, www.imim.com.au.

Cox H. ((2009) 'Expanding music-thanatology in the Geelong Region.' Report to United Way, Geelong Region, www.imim.com.au.

Cox H. (2010) 'The use of prescriptively played harp music in the Special Care Nursery.' Report to St John of God Hospital & The Annie Danks Foundation, www.imim.com.au.

Cripes L. (2011) 'The General' in *At the End of Life: True Stories About How We Die*, Lee Gutkind (ed). Creative Nonfiction Books, Pittsburgh.

Halifax JR. (2008) *Being With Dying: Cultivating Compassion and Fearlessness in the Presence of Death*. Shambhala, Boston.

Hollis J. (2010) *Music at the End of Life*. Praeger, California.

Karl, Rev J. (1992) 'Being there: Who do you bring to practice?' in *Presence of Caring in Nursing*, DA Gaut (ed) pp.1–13. New York: National League For Nursing Press.

References

Levine S. (1993) *Meetings at the Edge*. Gateway Books, Bath.

Lindholm L & Eriksson K. (1993) 'To understand and alleviate suffering in a caring culture.' *Journal of Advanced Nursing* 18:1354-61.

McNamara B. (2003) 'Good enough death: Autonomy and choice in Australian palliative care.' *Social Science & Medicine* 58(5): 929–938.

O'Donohue J. (1997) *Anam Cara*. Bantam Press, London.

Vaughan-Lee L. (1998) *Catching the Thread: Sufism, Dream-work and Jungian Psychology*. The Golden Sufi Center, www.goldensufi.org.

Rumi, (1995) *The Essential Rumi*. Coleman Barks (trans) with John Moyne, AJ Arberry & Reynold Nicholson. Harper-Collins, New York.